SHORT
RECEIVE

7 Oct-95 Maph. Cidiff
£2·95

by

R. A. Penfold

BERNARD BABANI (publishing) LTD
THE GRAMPIANS
SHEPHERDS BUSH ROAD
LONDON W6 7NF
ENGLAND

Please Note

Although every care has been taken with the production of this book to ensure that any projects, designs, modifications and/or programs etc. contained herewith, operate in a correct and safe manner and also that any components specified are normally available in Great Britain, the Publishers do not accept responsibility in any way for the failure, including fault in design, of any project, design, modification or program to work correctly or to cause damage to any other equipment that it may be connected to or used in conjunction with, or in respect of any other damage or injury that may be so caused, nor do the Publishers accept responsibility in any way for the failure to obtain specified components.

Notice is also given that if equipment that is still under warranty is modified in any way or used or connected with home-built equipment then that warranty may be void.

© 1991 BERNARD BABANI (publishing) LTD

First Published — January 1991

British Library Cataloguing in Publication Data
Penfold, R.A.
    Short wave superhet receiver construction.
    1. Shortwave radio equipment : Receivers. Construction
    I. Title
    621.38418

ISBN 0 85934 221 2

Printed and bound in Great Britain by Cox & Wyman Ltd, Reading

Preface

Short wave listening has been a popular hobby for many years now, and remains as interesting and absorbing as it ever was. Although ready-made "black boxes" have tended to dominate the hobby in recent years, the build your own approach remains popular, and seems to be undergoing a revival at present. Building your own set and using it to receive DX stations probably provides a greater degree of satisfaction than using the latest commercial digital wonder receiver.

"Simple Short Wave Receiver Construction" (BP275) describes some simple short wave sets of the tuned radio frequency (t.r.f.) and direct conversion varieties, complete with full constructional details. BP275 also provides some useful background information about short wave listening and the short wave bands. This book describes a more complex receiver of the superhet type, plus various add-on circuits that can be used to enhance the performance of the basic receiver. The finished receiver requires no complex alignment, and even in its basic form will provide world wide reception on both the broadcast and amateur bands. It should provide endless hours of fun for quite a modest monetary outlay.

The basics of short wave reception, project construction, etc. are not covered in this book. It is assumed that the reader has a reasonable background knowledge of both short wave radio and electronic project construction. It is strongly recommended that those who do not have the necessary background knowledge should study BP275 before trying to tackle the circuits featured in this publication.

R. A. Penfold

Other Titles of Interest

Contents

Chapter 1

THE SUPERHET RECEIVER

In the early days of amateur radio it was the norm for most of the equipment in the shack to be home constructed. Things gradually changed over the years, until it became the norm for practically all the equipment to be ready-made. Any home constructed equipment was likely to be in the form of a few minor accessories such as simple pieces of test equipment. This state of affairs probably still persists, with both radio amateurs and short wave listeners (s.w.l.s) tending to rely heavily on commercial "black boxes". However, there now seems to be something of a revival in home radio receiver construction.

Pros and Cons

It must be admitted that it is difficult for the home constructor to compete with ready-made equipment in terms of quality of finish. It is actually possible to achieve very high standards in this respect if you are reasonably skilful at this type of thing, and are prepared to put in the necessary time and effort. Being practical about it, a project that is an eyesore is unlikely to work any less well than one which has been given a standard of external finish that is the equal of the shiniest of ready-made "black boxes".

It is also difficult for the home constructor to compete with the sheer sophistication and complexity of modern communications equipment. Microprocessor control, frequency synthesis, and digital readouts seem to be standard features these days. These features are within the capabilities of advanced constructors, but probably few short wave enthusiasts are prepared to put in the time and effort needed to build a short wave set having a very advanced specification. Receivers of this type certainly go beyond the scope of this publication. The sets described herein lack the "frills" of most commercial receivers, but they nevertheless offer good performance. Again, being practical about it, many of the advanced features to be found on modern ready-made short wave sets greatly aid convenience in use, but do not really boost performance one iota. A home constructed short wave receiver, even a relatively simple one, can achieve a high level of performance.

Probably the main factor in favour of home constructed receivers is that they provide a greater feeling of achievement when some difficult DX station is picked up. You can feel, with some justification, that it was "all your own work". The same is perhaps not completely true when using the latest and most expensive ready-made equipment.

Another point in favour of home constructed receivers is that you can have a lot of fun building them. You can also learn a great deal from constructing and using your own radio equipment. It would be a mistake to regard construction of a receiver as a chore that must be got out of the way as quickly as possible so that you can get on with using the receiver. Electronic project building is an interesting and rewarding hobby in its own right. Many short wave enthusiasts who own sophisticated ready-made equipment try their hand at building short wave sets for the fun of building the units, and to see how the results obtained compare with expensive commercial gear. This is an aspect of the hobby that I avidly pursue, and it can provide some surprising results.

A home constructed receiver offers a relatively inexpensive means of obtaining a short wave set of good performance. The more simple ready-made communications receivers are, in absolute terms, quite sophisticated and expensive. This can make it difficult to get into the hobby with good equipment at a reasonable cost. Home constructed equipment offers one solution to the problem. For the less adventurous, older secondhand equipment offers about the only alternative. If you should decide to take this route, bear in mind that much of this equipment is reaching the stage where it will be much less reliable than it once was, and repairs could be expensive. In fact repairs could be virtually impossible if an unusual component becomes faulty.

The circuits provided in this book are all reasonably easy to construct, but no constructional details are provided. Ideally the receivers should be constructed on custom printed circuit boards, but plain matrix board with the components hard wired on the underside offers a good, simple alternative. Where applicable, construction notes are provided, pointing out any pitfalls that must be avoided. This book is not really intended for complete beginners to electronics construction. Anyone with a certain amount of practical experience at project construction should be able to build the designs without too much difficulty, but they are considerably less than ideal for complete beginners. Book No. BP275 ("Simple Short Wave Receiver Construction") covers more basic receivers, includes construction details, and represents a much more practical starting point for newcomers to the hobby.

Mixing It

With the only exceptions of a few inexpensive miniature receivers, all ready-made radio receivers are of the superheterodyne variety, or "superhets" as these sets are more commonly called. This is not really surprising, since superhet receivers offer what is in most respects much better performance than "straight" receivers (tuned radio frequency types, etc.). This higher performance is achieved at the cost of greater complexity, and superhets also need to be accurately aligned once completed if they are to give optimum performance. A badly setup superhet is likely to have a very low level of performance indeed. In fact it could well be totally unusable.

Ideally, a minimum of an accurately calibrated radio frequency (r.f.) signal generator and a multimeter are needed in order to align a superhet. In practice you can usually get superhets aligned satisfactorily without the aid of any test equipment whatever. The designs featured here can all be aligned without the aid of any test equipment, and full alignment details are provided. Things are much easier though, if suitable test equipment is to hand.

A superhet receiver differs from a tuned radio frequency (t.r.f.) type in that prior to detection the received signal is converted to an intermediate frequency (i.f.). A basic superhet receiver uses the arrangement shown in the block diagram of Figure 1.1. The mixer stage is central to the operation of a superhet receiver, and this is not a simple type, such as that used to mix two audio signals. The type of mixer used in a superhet is one that provides complex mixing,

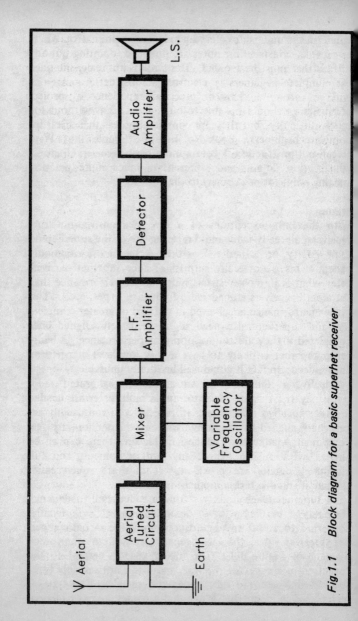

Fig. 1.1   Block diagram for a basic superhet receiver

4

and it does not simply produce an output signal that is the sum of the two input voltages.

Its action is most easily understood if it is considered in terms of the input and output frequencies. It generates sum and difference frequencies, and one or both of the input frequencies may appear at the output. With a double balanced mixer neither of the input frequencies appear at the output (apart from some low level breakthrough). They are removed by a balanced phasing process. In the case of a single balanced mixer, one of the input frequencies appears at the output while the other is suppressed. A simple non-balanced mixer permits both input frequencies to break through to the output. Any of these three types of mixer will work in a superhet, where it is the generation of the sum and difference frequencies that are all-important, rather than the suppression of the input frequencies. However, in a practical receiver there is some advantage in using a balanced mixer. The reasons for this are discussed later in this chapter.

The purpose of the mixer and oscillator stages is to convert the incoming signal, whatever its frequency, to the fixed intermediate frequency. In order to achieve this the oscillator must be tuned so that it is always above or below the input signal frequency by an amount that is equal to the intermediate frequency. In practice the oscillator is usually adjusted to track on the high frequency side of the reception frequency, but some receivers operate with the oscillator tracking below the reception frequency. The effect is much the same either way. For medium and long wave broadcast receivers the most popular intermediate frequencies are 455kHz, 465 kHz, and 470kHz (with 455kHz almost certainly being the most popular of these). However, for short wave receivers there are several other common intermediate frequencies, and some receivers operate with more than one intermediate frequency. For the moment we will assume that our example superhet receiver has a single intermediate frequency of 455kHz.

If the receiver tunes from (say) 2MHz to 8MHz, with the oscillator tracking on the high frequency side of the reception frequency, the oscillator must tune from 2.455MHz to 8.455MHz. The difference frequency then provides the required 455kHz intermediate frequency output (e.g. 2.455 MHz − 2.0MHz = 0.455MHz or 455kHz). Tuning the oscillator 455kHz below the reception frequency (1.545MHz to 7.545MHz) would also have the desired effect. Again, the difference frequency will provide the required 455kHz intermediate frequency output (e.g. 2.0MHz − 1.545MHz = 0.455 MHz or 455kHz). This mixing of two signals to produce a signal at a third frequency is called "heterodyning" incidentally, and it is from this that the superheterodyne (or just plain superhet) name is derived.

I.F. Stages

Converting the incoming signal to an intermediate frequency might seem like an unnecessary complication, but it provides great benefits. A t.r.f. receiver has to provide its gain and selectivity at the reception frequency. This is relatively difficult since a wide range of frequencies are covered by a short wave set, and the frequencies involved are quite high. With a superhet receiver the radio frequency gain and selectivity are relatively unimportant. Most of the gain and selectivity are provided at the intermediate frequency. High gain and selectivity are relatively easy to obtain at the fixed and (usually) quite low intermediate frequency.

One reason it is difficult to obtain high selectivity from a t.r.f. receiver is that utilizing a number of tuned circuits necessitates a section on the tuning capacitor for each of these tuned circuits. Using half a dozen or more tuned circuits is not very practical, with each one requiring a gang on the tuning capacitor. Obtaining high gain is also difficult due to the high frequencies involved. Obtaining high gain at high frequencies is not in itself a major problem, but maintaining stability with such a combination is problematic. The wiring to a number of tuning capacitor gangs encourages stray feedback and exacerbates the problem.

Matters are much easier with a superhet, where the fixed and relatively low intermediate frequency largely avoids these problems. Using a number of tuned circuits in order to obtain good selectivity is no problem, since each tuned circuit can have preset tuning. Intermediate frequency transformers are usually in the form of small coil units housed in aluminium screening cans that prevent problems with stray coupling from one transformer to another. In days gone by there were a few intermediate frequency transformers that were tuned via integral preset tuning capacitors, but all modern types are tuned via adjustable cores. The relatively low operating frequency of the tuned circuits mean that they have narrower bandwidths than tuned circuits of similar Q value working at the reception frequency.

Obtaining really good selectivity is not easy even when using several tuned circuits at a relatively low frequency. Rather than using dozens of tuned circuits, the normal solution to the problem is to use a special crystal, ceramic, or mechanical filter. These are not usable in t.r.f. receivers as they all have fixed operating frequencies. This obviously presents no difficulties with a superhet design, where the filter can be used in the intermediate frequency stages.

The degree of selectivity obtained is very much dependent on the particular filter used. The cheaper units, which are mostly simple ceramic devices, offer a level of performance that is roughly comparable to those obtained using ordinary intermediate frequency transformers. These are not really intended for use in communications equipment. The highest quality types, which are usually crystal or mechanical filters, offer very high levels of performance indeed. They tend to be quite expensive though. However, there are some ceramic and mechanical filters that are reasonably inexpensive but which offer quite high levels of performance. These are popular for use in home-made communications equipment. Even a superhet receiver that has only intermediate frequency transformers and no additional filtering will still offer better selectivity than a t.r.f. receiver.

Image Problems

If we return to the block diagram of Figure 1.1, the mixer and oscillator stages convert the incoming signals to the intermediate frequency, and the intermediate frequency amplifier then provides most of the receiver's gain and selectivity. A demodulator that is appropriate to the type of reception being undertaken is used to recover the audio signal from the output of the intermediate frequency amplifier. The audio signal is boosted by an audio frequency power amplifier and then fed to the loudspeaker or headphones.

A tuned circuit is used ahead of the mixer stage, and this is essential to the operation of the receiver. As described so far, a superhet might seem to be an ideal form of receiver, offering plenty of advantages with no drawbacks. Unfortunately, there is one major flaw in the superhet scheme of things. This is the various spurious responses of a superhet receiver. It will operate well on the reception frequency giving excellent sensitivity and selectivity, but it will also operate on several other frequencies!

Provided the receiver is sufficiently sophisticated, these spurious responses will only provide very weak reception. They will then rarely, if ever, become troublesome in practice. Many superhet receivers are not particularly sophisticated though, and in order to keep down the cost and complexity the filtering to combat unwanted responses is kept to a minimum. This can result in one or two of the spurious responses providing a level of sensitivity not that far removed from the sensitivity of the main response!

One spurious response occurs at the intermediate frequency. This is not usually a major problem since a single tuned circuit ahead of the mixer, plus the mixer itself, will usually reduce this response to an insignificant level. If problems should be experienced with intermediate frequency breakthrough, it is easily combatted using a simple wavetrap in the aerial lead. This is just a parallel tuned circuit in series with the signal path, so that it blocks signals at or close to its resonant frequency. It is adjusted to the intermediate frequency, and provides a very high level of attenuation.

Usually the most serious of the spurious responses is the image response. Consider our earlier example of a superhet receiver that tunes from 2MHz to 8MHz, has an intermediate frequency of 455kHz, and has the oscillator tracking above the reception frequency With the oscillator at 2.455MHz the receiver converts input signals at 2MHz to the 455kHz intermediate frequency (2.455MHz − 2.0MHz = 0.455MHz or 455kHz). The point to note here, is that a signal 455kHz above the oscillator frequency will also be converted to the

8

intermediate frequency (2.910MHz − 2.455MHz = 0.455MHz or 455kHz). The receiver therefore operates at the required reception frequency, and at a frequency that is higher than this by an amount which is double the intermediate frequency (910kHz in this example).

Obviously the tuned circuit at the input of the receiver will combat this image response, but it may not be very effective at doing so. The bandwidth of a single tuned circuit is quite wide. The bandwidth of a tuned circuit operating at a frequency near the upper limit of the short wave range (about 20MHz to 30MHz) is likely to be very wide indeed. The image response is likely to be quite weak at the low frequency end of the short wave range, although even here it may not be suppressed to the point where it will never cause any problems. At the high frequency end of the short wave spectrum the image response is likely to be attenuated very little at all. It might be as little at 12dB down on the main response.

It is not essential to do anything to combat the image response further, and receivers having poor image rejection can still provide quite good results. The image can be a real problem though. With a 455kHz intermediate frequency it is quite normal for reception on the 14MHz amateur band to be severely hindered by reception on the image response of powerful stations on a nearby broadcast band. Something more than a single tuned circuit should be used to combat the image response if a low intermediate frequency is used.

Adding a second tuned circuit will obviously help to reduce the image response, but will require an extra gang on the tuning capacitor. As two gangs are already needed in order to accommodate the aerial and oscillator tuning, this means that a three gang component will be needed. This is reasonable, and many receivers have two tuned circuits ahead of the mixer. These can be in the form of a simple twin tuned circuit filter, but would more commonly be in the form of a tuned circuit at the input, and another to provide the coupling between the radio frequency (r.f.) amplifier and the mixer stage. A radio frequency amplifier will not provide a massive increase in gain, but it can usually improve the performance of the receiver.

On the face of it there is no point in having a radio frequency amplifier, as slightly boosting the intermediate frequency gain would seem to offer an easier way of obtaining the same degree of sensitivity. In practice there is a definite limit to the amount of intermediate frequency gain that can be used, with any increase above this level simply giving a higher noise level. Although weak stations will be boosted in level, they will not be any more readable as they will not stand out any better above the higher background noise level. The main source of noise in most receivers is the mixer stage. As a radio frequency amplifier goes ahead of the mixer, it will not boost the mixer noise, and will give a useful boost to sensitivity. Of course, there is a limit to the amount of radio frequency gain that can be used without the background noise level rendering it ineffective. This occurs because more than a modest amount of radio frequency gain produces sufficient noise to swamp that produced by the mixer. The extra gain of a radio frequency amplifier, although relatively modest, is very worthwhile, especially on the high frequency bands where signal levels are often very low.

High I.F.

There is another means of improving image rejection, and this is to use a higher intermediate frequency. Remember that the image response is separated from the main response by an amount that is equal to twice the intermediate frequency. With an intermediate frequency of only 455kHz, this puts the image response less than 1MHz away from the main one. At one time 1.6MHz was a popular intermediate frequency for short wave receivers, but it seems to be relatively little used these days. It provides greatly improved image rejection since it puts the image some 3.2MHz above the main response. With two tuned circuits ahead of the mixer this gives reasonable attenuation of the image response right up to 30MHz. Many modern receivers use even higher intermediate frequencies that largely eliminate problems with the image response.

Using a higher intermediate frequency does produce one or two slight problems. One of these is that it is slightly more difficult to obtain the required amount of gain, although this is not really a major obstacle. Another problem is that a

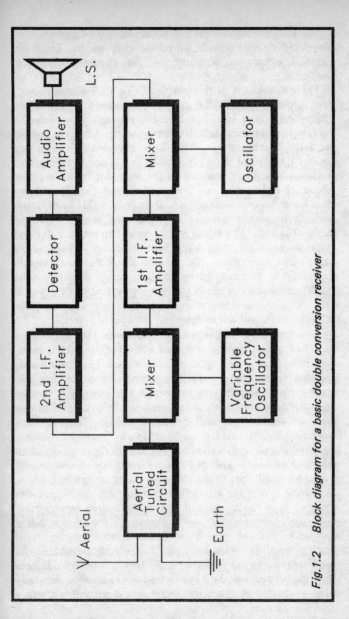

Fig.1.2   Block diagram for a basic double conversion receiver

11

higher intermediate frequency means that the bandwidth of the tuned circuits will be proportionately wider. Improved image rejection is obtained at the expense of poorer selectivity.

The old solution to this problem is to use a double conversion circuit. This is the arrangement shown in the block diagram of Figure 1.2. The incoming signals are converted to a high first intermediate frequency using the usual mixer/ oscillator combination. This high intermediate frequency ensures that good image rejection is obtained. A further mixer and oscillator stage, with the oscillator having a preset frequency in this case, are then used to take the signals down to a lower second intermediate frequency. This lower intermediate frequency permits high gain and selectivity to be easily obtained. The signal is then passed to the detector and audio stages in the usual way. Some receivers actually have a triple conversion circuit. This permits a high first intermediate frequency to be used, giving excellent image rejection. The third intermediate frequency can be very low (typically 100 kHz or less), enabling very high selectivity to be easily achieved, even without resorting to any special filters.

These multiple conversion arrangements can work quite well, but are something less than perfect. The extra conversion introduces more spurious responses. These additional spurious responses are usually relatively minor, but are still undesirable. Despite their shortcomings, multiple conversion receivers have been much used in the past, and in one form or another are still produced today. Most modern receivers do not use the basic setup of Figure 1.2 though. They often use quite complex systems that are designed to minimise problems with drift in the frequency of the variable frequency oscillator. Often they also utilize computer control, frequency synthesis, etc. Sets of this type go beyond the scope of this book, and will not be considered further here.

In the arrangement shown in Figure 1.2 the first oscillator is tunable, and the second one is at a fixed frequency. It is perhaps worth pointing out that it is perfectly possible to use the alternative setup of Figure 1.3. Here the first oscillator is at a fixed frequency, and the second one is tunable. Basically what we have here is a single conversion receiver that covers a

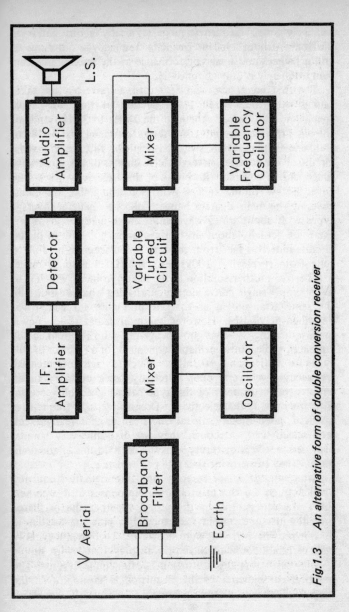

Fig.1.3   An alternative form of double conversion receiver

13

relatively small frequency range (typically about 2MHz to 3MHz). Although its intermediate frequency is quite low, it still achieves good image performance as the maximum reception frequency is only about 3MHz.

The first mixer and oscillator form a converter that takes signals over the desired 1MHz section of the short wave spectrum, and converts them to the 2MHz to 3MHz range of the basic receiver circuit. Using several switched first oscillator frequencies, plus several switched bandpass filters in the aerial circuit of the receiver, several 1MHz chunks of the short wave range can be covered. Receivers of this type sometimes only cover a few tuning ranges, with something like six bands covering the main amateur bands. Others are general coverage types with about thirty wavebands! With many modern sets there are actually about thirty wavebands, but built-in digital circuits hide this fact from the user. You seem to be able to tune from (typically) 100kHz to 30MHz in a single range.

There is another solution to the image problem, which is to use a simple single conversion circuit having what is essentially the same arrangement as the one in Figure 1.1 which was described previously. However, the intermediate frequency is made quite high so that good image rejection is obtained. A couple of typical intermediate frequencies for a receiver of this type are 9MHz and 10.7MHz. Such a high intermediate frequency gives very poor selectivity using ordinary tuned circuits, but a receiver of this type has a high quality crystal filter to provide the selectivity. Despite the high frequencies involved, good quality crystal filters can provide really excellent selectivity. Although they are basically very simple, provided receivers of this type have a crystal filter of adequate quality they can provide first rate performance.

Although the image response and intermediate frequency breakthrough are the main spurious responses of a superhet, there are others. In our theoretical superhet the oscillator provides just one output frequency, but practical oscillators do not provide perfectly pure sinewaves. There will inevitably be a certain amount of waveform distortion, and with simple $L - C$ oscillators this distortion is often quite severe. The practical consequence of this distortion is harmonics on the output of the oscillator. Harmonics are merely signals at multiples of the fundamental frequency. These can mix with incoming signals to produce a multitude of spurious responses. These spurious responses are at quite high frequencies well away from the main response, but suppression of them is often less than one might expect. I have encountered several receivers, including ready-made types, which suffer from breakthrough of powerful v.h.f. band II broadcast stations. However, these responses can usually be kept down to a level that prevents them from causing any major difficulties. Rather than relying on front end filtering, it is usually best to ensure that the oscillator provides a reasonably pure output.

There are other spurious responses that are caused by unwanted heterodyne effects. These can usually be kept down to an insignificant level without too much difficulty. Using a balanced or double balanced mixer helps to keep the number of frequencies in the system to a minimum, and removes some of these responses. Using a reasonably pure oscillator that is not at an excessive level also helps to keep these spurious responses down to an insignificant level.

A.G.C. Etc.

A practical short wave receiver is normally a little more complicated than the basic setup outlined in Figure 1.1. Figure 1.4 shows a typical arrangement for a simple short wave superhet receiver.

One refinement that has been added here is an automatic gain control (a.g.c.) circuit. Some of the output from the demodulator stage is heavily smoothed to give a d.c. level that is proportional to the strength of the received signal. This signal is fed back to the intermediate frequency amplifier stages, and possibly to the radio frequency amplifier as well, if such a stage is included. This signal is used to control the biasing of these amplifiers, and in the normal arrangement it is used to reduce the bias levels. The stronger the received signal, the greater the amplifier bias levels are reduced. The reduced bias levels give reduced gain from the amplifiers.

This gives a form of negative feedback, with the gain being reduced on strong signals so that they give an output level that is little higher than those from weak signals. This avoids

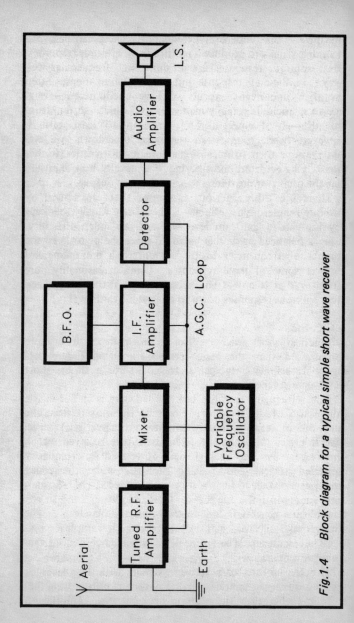

Fig. 1.4   Block diagram for a typical simple short wave receiver

16

having to make manual adjustments to the gain levels when tuning in stations of greatly differing signal strengths. Also, station fading is not exactly an unknown phenomena on the short wave bands. The automatic gain control will combat fading to some extent, but it will not be able to do anything about deep fades where there is no signal at all or an unusable signal level. Some a.g.c. circuits have two or more switched time constants, so that they can be set to respond rapidly or slowly to fading. This permits the a.g.c. circuit to be set so that it combats various types of fading in the optimum manner. For ordinary amplitude modulation (a.m.) reception a short time constant will usually give good results with any type of fading.

An ordinary a.m. diode demodulator is, of course, of no use for the reception of a single sideband (s.s.b.) or c.w. (continuous wave — a form of Morse code transmission). Ideally these require the use of a product detector plus a beat frequency oscillator (b.f.o.), or carrier insertion oscillator (c.i.o.) as it is alternatively known. Simple short wave receivers often lack a product detector, and instead have the output from the b.f.o. loosely coupled into the intermediate amplifier stages. This works quite well in that it gives a quite intelligible audio output from any s.s.b. signal of reasonable quality. It also gives good pure notes during c.w. reception. This system is considerably less than perfect though.

The main problems are centred on the a.g.c. circuit, and the effect of the b.f.o. signal on it. A high b.f.o. level must be used in order to guarantee that an s.s.b. signal will be demodulated properly, and low distortion level will be obtained. The b.f.o. signal must be at least as strong as the received signal in order to give a properly demodulated output. An inadequate b.f.o. level gives a very distorted sounding audio output. On the other hand, using a high b.f.o. level is undesirable as it results in the gain of the receiver being drastically reduced by the a.g.c. circuit.

The most simple solution is to keep the b.f.o. insertion level quite low, with the r.f. gain or aerial attenuator control being used to keep received signals down to a level that gives a properly demodulated output. As the a.g.c. circuit is effectively inoperative during s.s.b. and c.w. reception, an

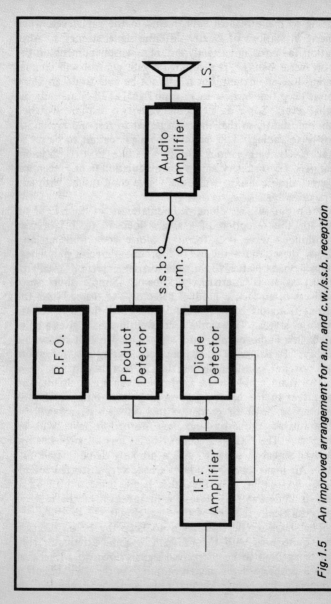

Fig.1.5 An improved arrangement for a.m. and c.w./s.s.b. reception

alternative method is to disable the a.g.c. action and use a higher b.f.o. level. The aerial attenuator or r.f. gain control must still be used to manually adjust the signal level in order to give an undistorted output at suitable volume. However, the setting of this control is less critical with a higher b.f.o. level.

If a product detector is included in the receiver, this problem is avoided completely. The demodulator, intermediate frequency, and audio stages would then be in the form shown in Figure 1.5. For a.m. reception the b.f.o. must be switched off, since there will otherwise be stray coupling of this signal into the intermediate frequency amplifier. This would generate unwanted heterodyne whistles. The a.m. demodulator and a.g.c. circuit function in the normal way, and the product detector is switched off or just ignored during a.m. reception.

For c.w. and s.s.b. reception the b.f.o. and product detector are activated, and the audio output signal is taken from the product detector. The a.m. demodulator is not needed for c.w./s.s.b. reception, but it is left in circuit so that the a.g.c. circuit can continue to function. Some receivers actually have a totally different a.g.c. circuit for c.w. and s.s.b. reception, possibly with the a.g.c. bias voltage being derived from the audio output of the product detector rather than the intermediate frequency output signal.

Finally

I suppose that a major drawback of DIY superhet receivers when compared to straight receivers is that they need to be aligned reasonably accurately in order to function properly. In other words, all the tuned circuits must be adjusted correctly or there will be problems with inadequate sensitivity, strong spurious responses, and a lack of selectivity. Alignment of the intermediate frequency stages is not usually too difficult. If no suitable test equipment is available, it is basically just a matter of adjusting the cores of the intermediate frequency transformers to peak a received station. Without the aid of a signal generator you can not be sure that the correct intermediate frequency has been set, but this is not usually important in practice. Having the intermediate frequency ten or twenty kilohertz higher or lower than it

19

should be is not going to have a significant affect on performance. If a crystal, ceramic, or mechanical filter is fitted to the receiver, this will dominate the selectivity, and ensure that precisely the correct intermediate frequency is obtained.

Alignment of the aerial, r.f., and oscillator stages is potentially more difficult. Without suitable test equipment it is difficult to set the receiver for the correct frequency coverage. You can simply accept whatever coverage the set has by default, perhaps making some adjustments later on if it becomes apparent that there is a lack of coverage at one end of the tuning range or the other.

Adjustment of the r.f., aerial, and oscillator stages is complicated by the fact that the r.f. and aerial tuned circuits have a slightly different frequency coverage to the oscillator tuned circuit. In fact the two coverages are very different on the low frequency bands, or if a high intermediate frequency is used. It is still not too difficult to adjust things so that these tuned circuits all track correctly, and if necessary it can be done without the aid of a signal generator.

Alternatively, front panel controls can provide fine tuning of the aerial and r.f. tuned circuits so that they can be kept accurately peaked without the need for any accurate alignment. Another alternative is to have separate tuning controls for the two or three front-end tuned circuits. This is not a particularly convenient way of handling things, but it is a low cost approach that practically eliminates the need for any alignment of the oscillator, r.f., and aerial tuned circuits. It enables the sensitivity of the receiver to always be maintained at maximum.

If you have suitable test equipment, then the superhet receiver circuits described in this book can be aligned quite easily. If access to suitable test gear is not possible, then it is worth reiterating that these circuits can still be set up satisfactorily. Alignment will be a little more difficult, and the exact frequency coverage of the receiver may not be known. These receiver designs will still be perfectly usable though, and will provide excellent results.

Chapter 2

BASIC S.W. SUPERHET

In this chapter a simple but effective short wave superhet receiver is described. Although it is not particularly sophisticated by current standards, it provides quite good results throughout the short wave range. The receiver's performance on the low frequency bands is somewhat better than that on the high frequency bands, but this is a factor that is common to most short wave receivers. In most respects its performance is substantially superior to the better tuned radio frequency (t.r.f.) receivers. It certainly achieves better sensitivity and selectivity, with this second aspect of performance being greatly aided by the use of a ceramic or mechanical filter. This set is much more convenient to use when compared to a t.r.f. receiver since there is no need to adjust a regeneration control in order to maintain the set at optimum performance.

This receiver is more complex and expensive than a simple t.r.f. set, but it is still very inexpensive to build when compared to ready-made communications receivers. It lacks the sophisticated features of these receivers, such as digital readouts and push-button frequency control, but its basic performance is quite good. It is certainly capable of receiving stations from all over the world, on both the amateur and broadcast bands. Even using quite a modest aerial, the prototype receiver has achieved this. The finished set does need a certain amount of alignment before it is ready for use, but it has been designed to make alignment very simple and straightforward.

The basic receiver is a simple superhet having a 455kHz intermediate frequency. The block diagram of Figure 2.1 shows the arrangement used in the receiver. There is a single tuned circuit at the input, a mixer stage with a separate oscillator, followed by two intermediate frequency amplifiers. A ceramic or mechanical filter provides the coupling between the two intermediate frequency stages, and it is this filter that largely controls the selectivity of the set. There are various filters that can be used here, and it is a matter of

21

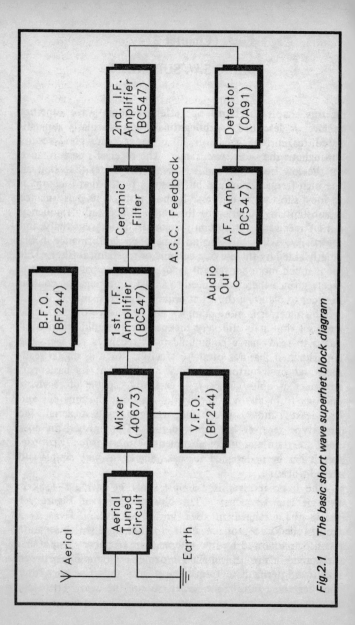

Fig.2.1   The basic short wave superhet block diagram

choosing the one that has the best characteristics for your intended modes of reception, and which also falls within your budget. Even one of the less expensive filters will provide excellent selectivity. The receiver is only equipped with a simple a.m. diode demodulator, but an optional b.f.o. permits c.w. and s.s.b. signals to be resolved quite well. A simple audio output stage provides good volume from a crystal earphone, high impedance headphones, or medium impedance headphones.

Although the basic receiver will provide good results, there is plenty of scope for improvement. Chapter 3 provides details of several additions and modifications that can be made to the basic design in order to enhance its performance and convenience in use. These include such things as an input attenuator/filter, an r.f. amplifier stage, a signal strength meter, and an improved audio output stage. Some of these are more useful than others. The input filter/attenuator or r.f. amplifier will substantially improve performance, and I would strongly urge the addition of one or other of these. An 'S' meter is less worthwhile, especially as its calibration will be more arbitrary than absolute. It is a popular feature of short wave sets though, and is one that most constructors will wish to include. It is up to the constructor to decide which add-ons, if any, should be included.

All the circuits have been designed so that, as far as reasonably possible, they use components that are widely available. Where it is not essential to use a particular component, alternatives are suggested, so that any potential supply difficulties are further eased. Discrete transistor circuits have been deliberately used in preference to dedicated integrated circuits in some instances, mainly because there are possible supply problems with radio integrated circuits. The transistors used in these circuits are all readily available, and are likely to remain so for a considerable period of time. Radio integrated circuits are more prone to problems with sudden disappearances, or replacement with improved but not fully compatible alternatives. For the home constructor, discrete transistor designs are probably an easier prospect anyway, and are somewhat less fussy about component layouts. Be warned though, that these are high gain circuits operating at quite high

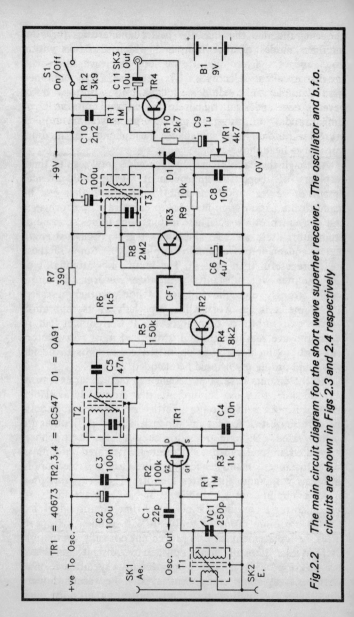

Fig. 2.2 The main circuit diagram for the short wave superhet receiver. The oscillator and b.f.o. circuits are shown in Figs 2.3 and 2.4 respectively

TR1 = 40673   TR2,3,4 = BC547   D1 = OA91

24

frequencies, and they inevitably require reasonable care to be taken over the component layouts.

The Circuit

Figure 2.2 shows the main circuit diagram for the basic short wave superhet receiver. The circuit diagrams for the local oscillator and b.f.o. stages are shown separately in Figures 2.3 and 2.4 respectively.

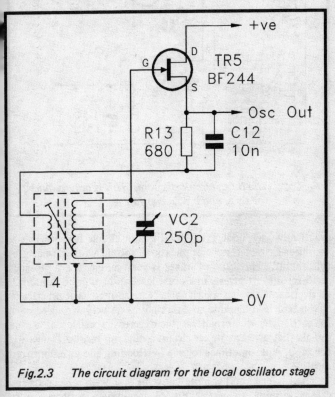

Fig.2.3   The circuit diagram for the local oscillator stage

If we take the main circuit first, the mixer stage uses a dual gate MOSFET (TR1). Although a 40673 is specified for the TR1 position, there are a number of more recent devices which should function properly in this circuit. In fact

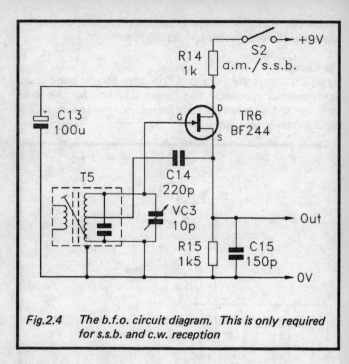

Fig.2.4   The b.f.o. circuit diagram. This is only required for s.s.b. and c.w. reception

practically any dual gate MOSFET intended for use in r.f. amplifier or mixer stage applications should work properly in this circuit. This type of mixer is very simple, but it provides good results. It gives a low noise level and has good immunity to overloading on strong signals. Note though, that practically any mixer is vulnerable to overloading on very strong signals. In particular, the broadcast bands provide masses of strong signals that give any mixer circuit a difficult task. Attenuating the input will sometimes reduce overloading and give improved results.

The mixer circuit is quite conventional, with R1 biasing the gate 1 terminal to earth, and R3 providing a positive bias to the source terminal (and hence a negative bias to gate 1). Dual gate MOSFETs are depletion mode devices, which means that they are normally switched on and require a reverse bias in order to take them into a part of their transfer characteristic

26

that will provide reasonably linear amplification. Together with their extremely high input resistances (typically about a million megohms), this gives them characteristics that are in many ways more like the old thermionic valves than ordinary bipolar transistors. Accordingly, their bias circuits are much like those used with valves. C4 bypasses R3 at high frequencies. This avoids the negative feedback and loss of gain that R3 would otherwise introduce.

Due to the very high input impedance of a MOSFET transistor, the tuned winding on input transformer T1 can be coupled direct to the gate 1 terminal of TR1. Due to its input capacitance, the input impedance of a MOSFET falls considerably at high frequencies. However, by having the tuned circuit coupled direct to gate 1 of TR1, this input capacitance effectively becomes part of the tuned circuit. Therefore, TR1 places minimal loading on T1, so that the input tuned circuit gives optimum rejection of any image signal. VC1 is the tuning capacitor for the aerial tuned circuit. The aerial is coupled to the input tuned circuit via a small coupling winding on T1.

The gate 2 terminal of TR1 is biased to the same potential as the source terminal (i.e. slightly positive) by R2. This gives good gain from the gate 1 terminal to the drain, but this gain is modulated by the oscillator signal. This signal is coupled to the gate 2 terminal of TR1 by C1. The resultant amplitude modulation of the input signal by the oscillator signal gives the required complex mixing that generates the all-important difference frequency. T2 is a single tuned intermediate frequency transformer, and this picks out the 455kHz intermediate frequency signal while filtering out the sum signal, breakthrough of the oscillator signal, etc.

I.F. Filtering
The intermediate frequency stages are fairly conventional, having two common emitter stages with coupling via a ceramic or mechanical filter. It is assumed in Figure 2.3 that the filter is a type which does not have input or output coupling transformers, and that it can therefore be connected direct to the output of TR2 and the input of TR3 without upsetting the d.c. bias conditions. If a filter having integral

coupling transformers is used, include 10n d.c. blocking capacitors in series with the input and output of the filter. Few filters seem to have built-in transformers these days, and none of the suggested filters are equipped with them.

The filter used in the prototype receiver is a Murata CFM455H (the Toko LFC6 is a broad equivalent to this). This is not primarily intended for communications purposes, but it gives quite good performance at low cost, and is a good choice for a simple short wave superhet receiver. Its minimum bandwidth at the −6dB point is 6kHz, while its maximum bandwidth at the −50dB point is 16kHz. However, bear in mind that these are worst case conditions, and that a typical filter will have much better response than these figures would suggest.

The bandwidth of the receiver has to be something of a compromise if the set is to be used for more than one reception mode. A bandwidth of about 6kHz or more is needed for ordinary a.m. reception. Around 3kHz or a little less is optimum for s.s.b., but is obviously inadequate for ordinary a.m. It is actually possible to receive a.m. signals properly with such a narrow bandwidth, but only if the i.f. filter is used to remove one sideband so that the signal can be received in the s.s.b. mode. A very good filter is needed in order to do this reasonably well, and the carrier suppression is still likely to be rather less than one would like. This method of a.m. reception, despite its potential advantages, is not very popular with broadcast band listeners.

The usual solution to the problem is to have a filter with a bandwidth of about 6kHz or so, and to simply put up with the wider than ideal bandwidth during s.s.b. reception. Despite the often crowded conditions on the amateur bands, a slightly wider than optimum bandwidth still permits quite good results to be obtained. A CFM455H filter offers a good low cost compromise for a.m./s.s.b. reception.

If higher performance is required, a Murata CFG455H (or Toko SLFD6) ceramic filter can be used. This gives a minimum bandwidth of 6kHz at the −6dB points, and a maximum of 18kHz at the −80dB points. If s.s.b. is likely to be the main mode used, then the CFG455I might be a better choice. This has a guaranteed minimum bandwidth of just 4kHz at the

−6dB points, but it would typically be something more like 5kHz to 6kHz. This is just about adequate for a.m. reception, and will give quite good speech quality. Receivers of this type are not really intended for music reception incidentally, and will give a rather muffled sounding output if used for the reception of music programs. The bandwidth of the CFG455I at the −80dB points is 10kHz, but would typically be significantly less than this. It therefore offers an excellent shape factor for what is a relatively inexpensive filter.

If your main interest is amateur bands reception and you are not too bothered about a.m. reception, then a filter specifically intended for s.s.b. reception can be used. A Murata CFM455JI should give good results (but I have not tested this filter in the receiver). This filter has a minimum bandwidth of 2.6kHz at the −6dB points, and a maximum bandwidth of 8kHz at the −50dB points. It therefore offers quite a good shape factor together with an adequate bandwidth for s.s.b. reception. There are higher quality 455kHz s.s.b. filters available, but they could be difficult to obtain. Also, their cost is likely to be disproportionate to the rest of the receiver.

It is, of course, possible to have separate filters for s.s.b. and a.m. reception. You can even have two filters for a.m. reception, one having the minimum acceptable bandwidth for use when band conditions are difficult, and one having a wider bandwidth (about 10 to 20kHz) for use when operating conditions permit such a wide bandwidth to be utilized. The switching is pretty basic, and a d.p.d.t. switch is all that is needed to switch between two filters.

However, in practice it is difficult to have more than one filter without compromising results. The filters are providing very high levels of attenuation outside the passband, but stray coupling in the wiring can easily bypass the filter and effectively reduce its performance. With just a single filter it is not too difficult to design a board layout that keeps this stray coupling to an insignificant level. With two or three filters and simple mechanical switching there will inevitably be some extra wiring that will encourage stray coupling around the selected filter. Another factor to bear in mind is that two or three filters of reasonably high performance will substantially boost the cost of the receiver (although this increased cost will bring some increase in performance). For a simple home constructed receiver a single i.f. filter having a good compromise bandwidth is probably the most practical solution.

For c.w. reception a very narrow bandwidth can be used, and will usually eliminate any adjacent channel interference even when band conditions are very crowded. Bandwidths as narrow as 100Hz or even less have been used, but a somewhat wider bandwidth is usually considered better. A slightly wider bandwidth will still give excellent immunity to adjacent channel interference, and makes any drift in the tuning less troublesome. Inexpensive i.f. filters having bandwidths as small as 100Hz to 200Hz would seem to be virtually unobtainable. If a suitable filter could be found, it would almost certainly be very expensive. This is not really too important as a simple and very inexpensive audio filter will provide excellent results for c.w. reception. There is actually some advantage in having the selectivity provided solely in the intermediate frequency stages, rather than by a combination of filtering in these stages and in the audio stages. This second approach is nearly as good though, and is certainly the more popular choice for home constructed short wave receivers.

A.G.C.

The output from the second intermediate frequency amplifier is coupled to the detector stage via a single tuned i.f. transformer. With only two tuned circuits in the intermediate frequency stages, and the selectivity largely provided by a ceramic or mechanical filter, this keeps the i.f. alignment very simple and straightforward indeed.

On the face of it, the intermediate frequency stages could be designed to avoid any conventional tuned circuits at all, with all the filtering provided by ceramic or mechanical filters. In practice this would not be a good idea. Ceramic and mechanical filters tend to have spurious responses at various frequencies, including harmonics of the fundamental operating frequency. Also, there are sometimes spurious responses at frequencies not too far removed from the passband.

It is normal to have at least a couple of conventional

tuned circuits in the intermediate stages in order to counteract any spurious responses of the main filter. Modern ceramic and mechanical filters have fewer and weaker spurious responses than most of their predecessors, but it is still advisable to have at least a couple of conventional i.f. transformers in the circuit.

The volume control (VR1) forms the resistive load for the demodulator, and C8 is the i.f. filter capacitor. Note that VR1 forms part of the bias circuit for the first intermediate frequency amplifier stage. Although in many circuits using a slightly different value for the volume control will often provide perfectly satisfactory results, this is not the case here. Using a different value would alter the biasing of TR2 and would almost certainly prevent the receiver from operating properly. The reason for including VR1 in the bias circuit of TR2 is that this enables a simple but effective a.g.c. action to be provided.

Note that this a.g.c. action relies on D1 being connected so that a negative d.c. bias is produced across VR1 by the smoothed i.f. half cycles. Although D1 will act as a demodulator whichever way round it is connected, note that it must be connected with the polarity shown in Figure 2.2 if the a.g.c. action is to be obtained. Getting its polarity wrong could well result in the receiver becoming unstable on strong signals.

The way in which the a.g.c. circuit operates is very simple. TR2 is biased by a potential divider chain which consists of R5, R4, R9, and VR1. Demodulated signals generate a negative bias across VR1, and this reduces the bias voltage fed to TR2. This results in a reduction in its collector current, and consequently causes a reduction in its gain as well. The stronger the received signal, the greater the negative bias voltage that is produced, and the greater the reduction in TR2's gain. This gives the required compression of the output level, with moderate and very strong signals giving virtually the same volume. Of course, weak signals will not produce a very high volume level, and no a.g.c. circuit can guarantee a perfectly uniform volume level. C6 is needed to remove the audio frequency signal on the a.g.c. bias voltage. The value of this capacitor controls the a.g.c. time constants. The

31

specified value gives quite a fast response time, and will give good results with most types of fading.

The audio amplifier is a simple high gain common emitter stage. This gives good volume from a crystal earphone, high impedance headphones, and most medium impedance headphones. It does not have sufficient drive for most low impedance headphones, and it is not suitable for use with low impedance (8 ohms) dynamic earphones either.

Power is obtained from a 9 volt battery, and the total current consumption of the receiver is only about 7 milliamps or so. A PP3 size battery is adequate, but if the receiver is likely to receive a great deal of use a higher capacity type would probably provide significantly lower running costs. A PP9 size battery or six HP7 size cells in a plastic holder are suitable if a higher capacity battery is to be used.

Oscillator/B.F.O.
The oscillator circuit (Figure 2.3) is a simple transformer feedback type. TR5 is a Jfet operated in the source follower mode, and it therefore has slightly less than unity voltage gain. T4 provides a voltage step-up from its low impedance primary winding to its tuned secondary winding, and the circuit therefore has sufficient feedback to sustain oscillation. The circuit does not oscillate particularly strongly, but it has a high enough output level to drive the mixer properly. The output is reasonably pure, and there are no really strong harmonics to produce strong spurious responses at high frequencies. VC2 is the oscillator tuning control, and is also the main tuning control for the whole receiver. It is the setting of this control that determines the reception frequency, not the setting of VC1. Adjustment of the latter permits received signals to be peaked, but does not significantly affect the reception frequency.

A BF244 is specified for TR5, and the circuit should work well with any version of this device (BF244A, BF244B, or just plain BF244). It should also work well with similar junction gate field effect transistors, such as the popular 2N3819. Like any oscillator circuit, this one will drift slightly with variations in the supply voltage and temperature. Despite its extreme simplicity, this circuit is quite stable though, provided a good quality component is used for VC2.

The b.f.o. circuit (Figure 2.4) uses a configuration that is similar to the one used in the local oscillator. In this case though, the feedback is taken to a tapping on the tuned winding, rather than to the low impedance coupling winding. Originally the coupling winding was used, but this was found to give unreliable oscillation. Using the tapping gives much better results. It was still found to be necessary to include C15 in order to obtain absolute reliability. This component also helps to attenuate the harmonics on the output of the b.f.o. It is important that these harmonics are kept down to a reasonably low level, as many of them are at frequencies within the coverage of the receiver. They are at 455kHz intervals, which means that they are few and far between, but it is always best to avoid the generation of spurious signals as far as possible.

VC3 is the b.f.o. tuning control. The core of T5 is set up so that VC3 enables the b.f.o. to be tuned up to a few kilohertz either side of the intermediate frequency. For lower sideband reception the b.f.o. is tuned to the high frequency side of the intermediate frequency – for upper sideband reception it is tuned to the low frequency side. For c.w. reception the offset can be in either direction, and it is just a matter of selecting the one that gives the best freedom from adjacent channel interference.

There is some advantage in having the b.f.o. tunable, rather than simply having switched frequencies for upper and lower sideband reception. With perfect i.f. filtering there would in fact be no point in having a tunable b.f.o. The optimum b.f.o. frequencies for upper and lower sideband reception would be very well defined. As this receiver will be fitted with something less than optimum s.s.b. filtering, the optimum b.f.o. frequencies are less well defined. There will be a small range of frequencies that will provide perfectly good audio output quality. In use you will sometimes find that adjacent channel interference can be reduced by shifting the b.f.o. frequency slightly and retuning the receiver. Do not be tempted to shift the b.f.o. frequency too far off its normal setting. Setting it too far in one direction will attenuate the low frequencies in the audio output signal, while excessive adjustment in the opposite direction will result in a loss of high frequencies on the audio output.

If you would prefer switched upper and lower sideband operation, despite the limitations of this method, it is easily achieved. Simply replace VC3 by a trimmer of about 10p in value, connected in series with a s.p.s.t. switch. With the switch open, adjust the core of T1 to set the b.f.o. frequency slightly on the high frequency side of the intermediate frequency. Then close the switch and adjust VC3 to set the b.f.o. frequency just on the low frequency side of the intermediate frequency. The section of this chapter which deals with alignment discusses ways of determining the correct b.f.o. frequencies if no test equipment to aid this task is available. Having switched b.f.o. frequencies means that there is no quick means of trimming the frequency to compensate for any drift. This b.f.o. circuit seems to be very stable though, and it is unlikely that any problems with drift will be encountered.

The output from the b.f.o. is from the source terminal of TR6. Note that this does not actually connect to anything in the main receiver (unless you construct the product detector described in Chapter 3). An insulated wire connected to the output of the b.f.o. and placed near the i.f. stages of the receiver is all that is needed in order to obtain a high enough coupling of the b.f.o. signal into the i.f. amplifiers. S2 is the b.f.o. on/off switch, and is effectively the a.m./s.s.b. mode switch.

Band Changing
The receiver is designed to use Toko coils which have printed circuit mounting bases. In the past it was common practice for home constructed short wave receivers to use plug-in coils. The receiver would either be constructed with an open aluminium chassis and front panel, or in a metal case having a hinged lid. Either way, this gave easy access to the interior of the receiver so that the coils could be easily unplugged and plugged in, and band changing could be achieved. An alternative method which I found to be quite good was to have the coils mounted so that they were slightly protruding through holes in the top or rear of the case. Again, this permitted them to be easily removed and replaced in order to

facilitate band changing. Unfortunately, the various ranges of plug-in coils that were once freely available no longer seem to be produced.

This does not mean that plug-in band changing is no longer possible. I have found that it is quite easy to mount a Toko printed circuit mounting coil onto a plug, such as a 5-way DIN type. This effectively converts it into a plug-in type, which can then be used with a socket of the appropriate type.

There are three sets of coils which between them cover the entire short wave range. The approximate coverage of each range is as follows:—

Range 1 — 1.7MHz to 5MHz

Range 2 — 5.5MHz to 14MHz

Range 3 — 12MHz to 30MHz

It has to be emphasised that these frequency coverages are only approximate. The exact coverages depends on the settings of the cores in the oscillator coils. They also depend on the value of the tuning capacitors. A value of 250p is specified for VC1 and VC2 in the components list, but this is the minimum acceptable value. Higher value components (such as 300p and 365p types) are perfectly suitable, but will give somewhat extended low frequency coverage. This table gives the Toko part numbers for T1 and T2 on all the three ranges.

Range	Aerial/R.F. (T1)	Oscillator (T2)
1	KANK3333R	KANK3426R
2	KANK3334R	KANK3337R
3	KANK3335R	KANK3428R

I suppose that the reason for using plug-in band changing is something less than obvious. It might appear that band switching would in many ways be an easier prospect. One problem with band switching on a short wave superhet is that there are a number of windings to be switched, necessitating the use of a switch having a substantial number of poles. At one time there were switch kits available which enabled quite complex wafer switches (a form of rotary switch) to be made up. These could have practically any desired number of ways and poles. Suitable switches would seem to be more difficult to obtain these days. In the past and now, even if a suitable switch can be located, it is likely to be quite expensive.

A second, and potentially more serious problem, is that of keeping all the wiring suitably short. There are two reasons for keeping the wiring as short as possible. One of these is simply that long wires tend to encourage instability, and generally poor performance. The second, and probably more crucial reason, is that long wires will affect the frequency coverage of the receiver. Long wires to the tuned windings effectively become extensions of the windings, giving a boost to their inductance. The practical result of this is that the frequency coverage tends to be shifted in the low frequency direction.

The problem is more severe on the high frequency range than on the middle and low frequency ones. This is due to the comparatively small inductances involved on the high frequency range. The small amount of inductance in the wiring can be quite large when compared to that of a high frequency coil. On the low frequency range the effect of the wiring might not be very significant. On the middle range it is likely to be quite noticeable, but adjusting the cores of the coils might make it possible to obtain the right frequency coverage. On the highest frequency range any long wiring to the tuned windings is likely to leave the frequency coverage at least a few megahertz short of the 30MHz upper limit of the short wave spectrum.

It must be emphasised that by long wiring I do not mean wires of a few hundred millimetres or more in length. Even 50 millimetres of wiring can give problems, and ideally so-called "leadless" construction techniques would be used. These leadless techniques, or something approximating to them, are not difficult to use if the receiver is built as a single band type, or with plug-in band changing. With a single band receiver the coils can be mounted on a printed circuit board, plain matrix board, or whatever, and there should be no difficulty in keeping the wiring very short. The only point to watch with this method is that the wires from the circuit board to the tuning capacitors are kept quite short. Remember that long wires to the tuning capacitors effectively gives variable capacitors with inductors wired in series, and that these inductors will prevent the tuning capacitors from giving the correct frequency coverages.

With plug-in band changing the conventional set-up is to have the sockets for the coils mounted on an aluminium chassis. Solder-tags fitted on the mounting bolts for the sockets can then provide convenient earthing points. The mixer and oscillator circuits can then be wired up on the sockets using what is essentially the same method of construction that was popular with valved circuits about thirty or more years ago. It is helpful to use sockets having more pins than the coil requires so that there are some spare pins to accommodate all the connection points. The rest of the receiver can be constructed on a circuit board in the usual way. Although this method might seem to be rather old fashioned, it is an eminently practical method of construction for this type of receiver. It is certainly a method of construction that I would wholeheartedly recommend.

. If band switching is to be used, either the point to point style of wiring or a circuit board can be used. Either way, the physical layout of the receiver must be such that the wiring to the switch can be kept very short. It is not normally necessary to switch both leads of each winding. It is unlikely that there will be any problems if just one side of each winding is switched, and this should be the non-earth side of each winding. In the case of aerial coupling windings you can usually get good results if these windings are simply connected in series, with no switching being used. Thus, band switching for the basic version of this receiver can be accomplished using a three-way three-pole switching using the system shown in Figure 2.5.

The rest of the receiver is far less critical, and is easily constructed on a custom printed circuit board or plain matrix board. If you are not into DIY printed circuit boards, then plain matrix board offers a simple but effective alternative.

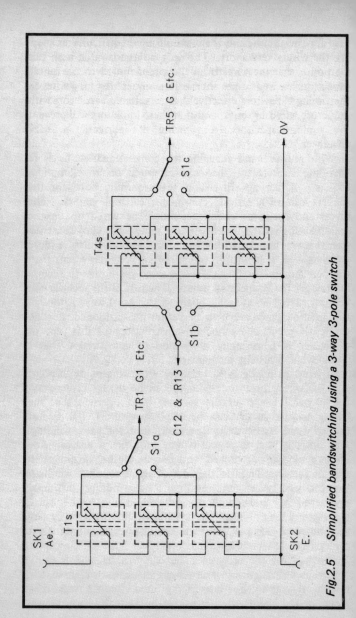

Fig.2.5 Simplified bandswitching using a 3-way 3-pole switch

This method of construction seems to be little used these days, but it is one that is very good for radio receivers. I would not recommend stripboard for this type of project as the capacitance between the copper strips can give problems with stray coupling. The relatively high frequencies involved in the intermediate frequency stages plus the high gain of the set makes the unit vulnerable to instability due to stray feedback. A carefully designed stripboard layout can give good results with a receiver of this type, but it is difficult to design a layout that can be guaranteed to work well.

It is essential that the connections to the r.f. transformers and i.f. transformers are correct. The phasing of some windings is important, and the oscillator will not function, for example, if T4 is connected in such a way that it inverts the signal. Note that the tappings on the tuned windings are not centre taps, and that where appropriate, it is essential to use the correct end of the winding in conjunction with the tapping. To avoid any errors when dealing with the coils, follow the methods of connection shown in Figure 2.6. Note that these are top views (which is the logical choice, as circuit layouts are normally designed as viewed from the component side). Connection details for the i.f. filters are also provided in Figure 2.6, but the suggested types are all symmetrical, and can actually be used either way round.

As each range of the receiver covers quite a wide frequency span, and the selectivity is quite good, it is essential to have some form of bandspread. This is especially important if you will be using the receiver for s.s.b. reception, which requires very precise tuning. If mechanical bandspread is used, at the very least VC2 should be fitted with a slow motion drive having a reduction ratio of 36 to 1. Suitable drives seem to be unobtainable these days, and most slow motion drives only seem to offer a reduction ratio of around 6 to 1, or about 10 to 1 at best. Provided the drive is fitted with a fairly large control knob, this should just about be satisfactory for a.m. reception. It is unlikely to be good enough for s.s.b. reception though, especially on the high frequency bands.

Probably the best solution to the problem is to fit VC2 with a slow motion drive having a reduction ratio of about 8 to 1, and to add a fine tuning control. This can simply consist

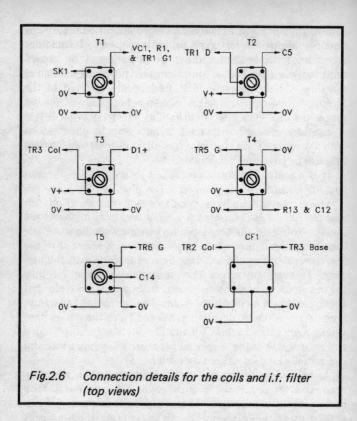

*Fig.2.6   Connection details for the coils and i.f. filter
(top views)*

of a 5p variable capacitor wired in parallel with VC2. This
effectively gives a reduction ratio of about 50 to 1 or more.
Adding a fixed capacitor of about 4p7 in series with the 5p
variable will reduce its effective value, giving an effective
reduction ratio of over 100 to 1. This should make fine
tuning on s.s.b. signals reasonably easy, even on the high
frequency bands. In order to obtain really fine control, fit
the fine tuning control with a slow motion drive. Note that
the tuning of VC1 is much broader than that of VC2, and
that it does not require a slow motion drive or a fine tuning
control.

TR1 is a MOS device, and as such it is vulnerable to static

charges. The 40673 has no built-in protection diodes, but is normally supplied with a metal clip or a piece of wire that short circuits its leadout wires to its metal case. This should be left in place until construction has been completed, and it will then totally eliminate any risk of static damage to the component. Some alternative devices also have this shorting wire or clip, and should be treated in the same way. A few devices have built-in protection circuits and no shorting clip or wire. These can be treated much like other semiconductors, but they should be handled no more than is really necessary. They should be soldered into circuit using a soldering iron having an earthed bit.

The OA91 diode specified for D1 is a germanium device. Silicon diodes are unsuitable for this application as their forward voltage drops are too high. Germanium semiconductor components are more vulnerable to heat damage than are the more familiar silicon types. Accordingly, a little more care than usual should be exercised when soldering D1 into place. It should not be necessary to use a heat-shunt, but each soldered joint should be completed reasonably swiftly.

Alignment

Alignment of the radio frequency circuits is largely avoided by using separate (not ganged) tuning capacitors for the aerial and oscillator tuned circuits. The core of T4 only needs to be adjusted if the frequency coverage provided is incorrect. If a calibrated signal generator or other suitable test gear is available, it should not take long to get the coverage of each tuning range corrected.

If you do not have access to test gear which can be used to check frequency coverage, any significant errors should come to light in use. Any errors of this type should soon become apparent, as there will be a broadcast or amateur band that should be receivable, but which is absent from the receiver's coverage. You might also find that a band which should not be within the coverage of the range in question can actually be received. Some adjustment of T4's core together with some trial and error should soon have the coverage corrected.

It is worth making the point that the cores of r.f. and i.f. transformers should only be adjusted using a proper trimming

41

tool. Small screwdrivers are considerably less than ideal for this type of thing. The metal blade can significantly affect the inductance of the coil. The adjustment might be right while the screwdriver is in place, but it will effectively shift as the screwdriver is removed from the core. Of greater importance, the wedge shape of most screwdriver blades can easily lead to the brittle ferrite cores of the coils chipping or cracking. In a minor case a small piece of the core will chip away, but the coil will still function perfectly. If things go badly wrong the core will crack into two parts, and will jam inside the former. Trimming tools are not expensive, and should be considered essential items for anyone who is interested in building radio receivers.

VC1 is used to peak received signals, but it may be found that with VC2 adjusted close to its maximum or minimum value, VC1 can not be used to peak signals properly. The core of T1 should then be adjusted to correct this, so that VC1 can peak signals with VC2 at any setting. Some trial and error should soon locate a suitable setting for T1's core.

Because the bandwidths of T2 and T3 are quite wide, the receiver should work to some extent before these two transformers are aligned properly. Tune in any station as accurately as possible, and then adjust the cores of these two components to peak the signal. The 'S' meter described in Chapter 3 makes adjusting the cores to accurately peak signals much easier. Remember that the receiver has automatic gain control, and that large variations in the strengths of received signals have little effect on the audio output level.

As an alternative to using the 'S' meter circuit, a multimeter can be used to monitor the voltage across C6. Note that peak signal level corresponds with minimum voltage across C6. A further alternative is to use a weak station that will not activate the a.g.c. circuit. The cores of the i.f. transformers can then simply be adjusted for maximum volume. Once the cores of T2 and T3 have been peaked, retune the station and readjust the cores of T2 and T3. Repeat this process a couple of times, and the i.f. stages should then be very accurately aligned.

Last i.f. stages sometimes have a tendency to go into oscillation when the core of the last i.f. transformer is peaked. It is possible to add components to damp the oscillation, but it is not really necessary to do so in this case, should the instability problem arise. As the selectivity is provided mainly by the i.f. filter, not the i.f. transformers, simply leaving T3 slightly off the peak setting will avoid the oscillation, but will not affect performance to a significant degree.

In order to align the b.f.o. tune in an a.m. station as accurately as possible, and set VC3 at a mid setting. Switch on the b.f.o., and adjust the core of T5 to obtain a heterodyne whistle, if one is not already present. Once the heterodyne tone has been obtained, it should be possible to alter its pitch by adjusting the core of T5. Adjust T5 for the lowest pitch that can be obtained. Adjusting VC3 either side of its central setting should then produce an increase in pitch. You should find that as VC3 is adjusted for a higher pitch, the audio signal is initially quite strong. Above a certain pitch the signal will rapidly fall in strength. The same effect should be noticed whichever direction VC3 is offset. The optimum settings for s.s.b. reception are at the points where this drop in volume commences, or just slightly short of these settings.

As explained previously, the b.f.o. injection level has to be something of a compromise. A low level gives good sensitivity, but strong signals will produce quite high levels of distortion on the audio output signal. A high level gives low distortion, but operates the a.g.c. circuit and gives greatly reduced sensitivity. Probably the best solution is to use a fairly low level, and to include either the r.f. amplifier or input filter described in Chapter 3. These both include input attenuators that enable strong signals to be backed-off to the point where audio distortion is avoided.

Alternatively, a 1k potentiometer could be added at the input of the receiver to act as a simple aerial attenuator, as in the r.f. amplifier and input filter circuits. However, I would strongly recommend using the amplifier or filter circuit, rather than simply adding a variable attenuator. The additional tuned circuits of these circuits significantly reduce problems with the image response and overloading of the mixer when there are a lot of strong signals on the band you are using. The level of b.f.o. injection is controlled by placing an insulated wire connected to the output of the b.f.o. near to the first i.f. amplifier stage. It is placed closer to increase the b.f.o. injection level, or further away in order to reduce it. A little trial and error should soon locate a suitable b.f.o. level.

The receiver requires the usual long wire aerial. It is quite sensitive and will provide quite good results using a short indoor aerial. As with any receiver though, a long outdoor aerial is preferable for operation on the low frequency bands, or when propagation conditions are poor. An earth connection is not essential, but can substantially boost signal strengths on the low and middle frequency bands.

Components (including optional b.f.o.) for Figures 2.2, 2.3 and 2.4

Resistors (all 0.25 watt 5% carbon film)

R1	1M
R2	100k
R3	1k
R4	8k2
R5	150k
R6	1k5
R7	390R
R8	2M2
R9	10k
R10	2k7
R11	1M
R12	3k9
R13	680R
R14	1k
R15	1k5

Potentiometer

VR1	4k7 log carbon

Capacitors

C1	22p ceramic plate
C2	100μ 10V elect
C3	100n ceramic
C4	10n polyester
C5	47n polyester
C6	4μ7 63V elect

C7	100μ 10V elect
C8	10n polyester
C9	1μ 63V elect
C10	2n2 polyester
C11	10μ 25V elect
C12	10n polyester
C13	100μ 10V elect
C14	220p polystyrene
C15	150p polystyrene
VC1	250p air spaced variable
VC2	250p air spaced variable
VC3	10p air spaced variable

Semiconductors

TR1	40673 or similar dual gate MOSFET
TR2	BC547
TR3	BC547
TR4	BC547
TR5	BF244 or similar N channel Jfet
TR6	BF244 or similar N channel Jfet
D1	OA91

Miscellaneous

T1	Toko s.w. r.f./aerial coil (see text)
T2	Toko YRCS11098AC or similar 1st i.f.t.
T3	Toko YHCS11100AC or similar last i.f.t.
T4	Toko s.w. oscillator coil (see text)
T5	Toko YRCS11098AC or similar 1st i.f.t.
S1	s.p.s.t. min-toggle
S2	s.p.s.t. min-toggle
B1	9 volt battery (PP3 size — see text)
SK1	Red 4mm socket
SK2	Black 4mm socket
SK3	3.5mm jack or similar 2-way audio type
CF1	455kHz ceramic or mechanical filter (see text)
	Slow motion drive (see text)
	Case
	Medium — High impedance headphones or crystal earpiece

Circuit board
Four control knobs
Wire, solder, etc.

The Toko coils and the Murata i.f. filters are available from:

Cirkit,
Park Lane,
Broxbourne,
Herts EN10 7NQ.

Chapter 3

ADD-ON CIRCUITS

The basic short wave superhet described in Chapter 2 has quite a good level of performance, but its performance is easily enhanced by some simple add-on circuits. Several circuits of this type are featured in this chapter. The circuits covered include such things as an r.f. amplifier, a product detector, an 'S' meter, and an improved audio output stage. Some of these circuits enhance the performance of the receiver, while others make it easier to use rather than genuinely improving its performance. Some of the circuits are straightforward additions to the original design, while others replace some of the original circuitry. For example, the audio power amplifier circuit replaces the original single transistor stage, it is not simply tagged onto the original audio stage.

Where any changes to the original design are required, they are described in the text, with extra information being supplied in the diagrams where necessary. As this is not a book for complete beginners to electronics construction and short wave radio, it is assumed that the reader understands the basic principles involved, and will have no difficulty in sorting things out. Those without the necessary background knowledge and experience will need to read the text and study the diagrams more carefully, but all the information needed is there if you look for it!

Input Filter

One of the weakest aspects of the original design is its lack of good image rejection on the high frequency bands. As radio traffic on the high frequency bands is often, to say the least, a bit sparse, the lack of performance in this respect is often not very noticeable. Problems are most likely to be noticed at frequencies of around 10MHz to 15MHz where there are often a great many powerful stations, and the image rejection of the receiver is not terribly good. The most simple way of improving the image performance is to add another tuned circuit ahead of the mixer stage. This will not give massive attenuation of the image response at the highest reception frequencies, but it will give quite high attenuation over the important 10MHz to 15MHz range. An aerial tuning unit can be used to give a further reduction in the image response, and other spurious responses.

Using a higher first intermediate frequency plus a double conversion technique would give even better image rejection, but getting everything aligned properly would then become much more difficult. Also, double conversion techniques can easily generate new spurious responses without dealing completely effectively with the original ones. For a relatively simple short wave receiver for the home constructor it is probably best to settle for a single conversion set having a 455kHz intermediate frequency, and to accept that the receiver will have something less than the ultimate in image rejection on the high frequency bands. With two tuned circuits ahead of the mixer, plus perhaps a third in the form of an aerial tuning unit, results should be perfectly adequate.

The circuit diagram for the input filter appears in Figure 3.1. The new components are VR1, T1, and VC1, which are added ahead of T1 and VC1 of the original receiver circuit. The aerial socket, SK1, is of course part of the original receiver circuit, and it is relocated in the new setup. The circuit is very straightforward, and the signal is simply taken through an extra r.f. transformer before being applied to the primary winding of T1 in the original circuit. The output from the tuned winding of the additional r.f. transformer is taken from a tapping on the tuned winding. This avoids excessively loading the tuned circuit, which would effectively reduce its Q value and widen its bandwidth. As this circuit is purely passive it will not provide any gain, and will in fact reduce sensitivity slightly. However, its benefits considerably outweigh any slight loss of sensitivity it produces.

VR1 is an input attenuator control, and it is just a simple volume control style variable attenuator. Although there may seem to be little point in reducing the input signal level, this is actually a very useful addition to the receiver. As pointed out in the previous chapters, there can be problems with the reception of s.s.b. signals due to the b.f.o. activating the a.g.c. circuit. The best solution to the problem is to use a product

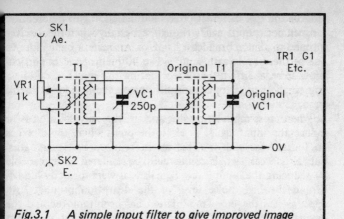

Fig.3.1   A simple input filter to give improved image performance

detector rather than relying on a simple diode demodulator plus a loosely coupled b.f.o. signal. A suitable product detector design is featured elsewhere in this chapter. However, if a product detector is not fitted, an input attenuator enables s.s.b. signals to be kept down to a level where they fail to overload the b.f.o. signal and produce strong distortion.

An input attenuator can also be useful at combatting cross modulation. This is a fairly involved subject, but if an r.f. amplifier or mixer stage becomes overloaded, it will generate strong distortion products. This can lead to cross modulation, which sometimes lives up to its name. While listening to one a.m. station, you also hear a second station on a nearby frequency. In effect, the modulation from one station is being superimposed on the carrier wave of a second station, and you hear two stations simultaneously. In practice the results of cross modulation do not always assume this clear-cut form. The overloading will often be caused by dozens of very strong signals, with countless strong distortion products being generated in consequence. The practical result of this is that the receiver seems to lack sensitivity, and there is a very high noise level when tuning between strong stations.

The additional tuned circuit ahead of the mixer helps to cut down the number of signals that reach the mixer, and reduces the risk of severe cross modulation. Cross modulation can still occur quite easily though, especially when the receiver is tuned to a main broadcast band, or an amateur band close to one of these broadcast bands. The 40 metre band in particular, can be a difficult prospect during the hours of darkness due to the very strong transmissions on the nearby 41 metre band.

When cross modulation does occur, the only solution is to reduce the input signal level to the point where the mixer is no longer overloaded. This means reduced signal strengths, but fairly weak signals can actually be rendered more readable by reducing the input level. Signals that were formerly hidden behind the high noise level of the distortion products can appear once the cross modulation has been removed and the distortion has gone. In some cases signals that were not previously detectable at all will become perfectly readable. Obviously very weak signals will not be readable after the input level has been backed-off, as they will be reduced to an insignificant level. Nothing will have been lost by reducing the signal level though, since these signals would not be readable through the high noise level anyway. You just have to accept that these stations are beyond the capabilities of the receiver under difficult band conditions.

VC1 can be a single gang component, but the receiver will be easier to use if it is ganged with VC1 of the original receiver circuit. Alignment of the two aerial tuned circuits should present no difficulty. Simply tune to a station and then adjust the cores of the two coils for maximum signal strength. There is likely to be a certain amount of interaction between the two tuned circuits, and it is therefore advisable to repeat this process a few times to ensure that they are both accurately peaked. The two tuned circuits should track accurately since they are virtually identical and cover identical frequency ranges.

Components for Figure 3.1

Potentiometer
VR1   1k lin carbon potentiometer

Capacitor
VC1   250p air spaced variable (see text)

Miscellaneous
T1   Toko range 1, 2, or 3 r.f./aerial coil, as
               required
               Wire, solder, etc.

R.F. Amplifier

An r.f. amplifier represents another means of adding an extra
tuned circuit ahead of the mixer, and it also provides a certain
amount of gain. It does not boost the sensitivity of the
receiver very much, but it can provide a worthwhile increase
in performance. The circuit diagram for the r.f. amplifier
stage appears in Figure 3.2. Like the input filter circuit, this
one requires the aerial socket (SK1) of the original circuit to

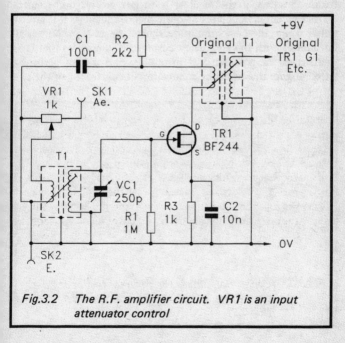

Fig.3.2   The R.F. amplifier circuit. VR1 is an input
           attenuator control

be slightly relocated. It also requires the primary winding of T1 in the original receiver circuit to be rewired. This now connects into the output circuit of the r.f. amplifier.

The circuit is basically just a simple common source stage based on a junction gate field effect transistor (TR1). A Jfet offers quite good gain, together with good noise and cross modulation performance. T1 is an additional r.f. transformer. This is tuned by VC1 (which should preferably be ganged with VC1 of the original receiver circuit), and it feeds direct into the very high input impedance of TR1. R1 provides gate biasing, while R3 and C2 are respectively the source bias resistor and bypass capacitor. R2 and C1 provide filtering in the positive supply line, and this helps to avoid instability. VR1 is a variable input attenuator. The increased gain ahead of the mixer means that there is an increased risk of problems with cross modulation. This control is consequently more important if the r.f. amplifier stage is used, and it is essential to use it wisely if the receiver is to give really good results.

As this circuit operates at quite high frequencies it is essential to keep all the wiring quite short. Apart from potential difficulties with the frequency coverage if long wires are used, there is also a possibility of instability or a lack of performance. Figure 3.3 provides connection details for T1 of the r.f.

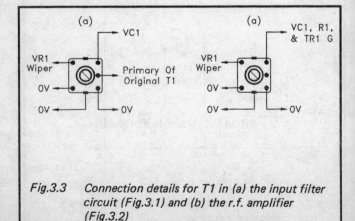

Fig.3.3   Connection details for T1 in (a) the input filter circuit (Fig.3.1) and (b) the r.f. amplifier (Fig.3.2)

amplifier, and also for T1 of the input filter circuit. Alignment of the two r.f. transformers is achieved in the same way as alignment of the input filter circuit described previously. Again, there should be no difficulty with any mistracking of the two tuned circuits, as they are virtually identical and cover the same frequency ranges.

If you wish, the r.f. amplifier can be added to the receiver, with the input filter circuit then being added ahead of this. If this should be done, it is obviously only necessary to include one of the variable attenuator controls. Ideally the three aerial/r.f. tuned circuits should be tuned by a three gang variable capacitor. With three tuned circuits ahead of the mixer the image rejection should be quite respectable, even on the high frequency bands. Cross modulation performance should also be quite good.

Components for Figure 3.2

Resistors
R1   1M 0.25 watt 5% carbon film
R2   2k2 0.25 watt 5% carbon film
R3   1k 5% 0.25 watt carbon film

Potentiometer
VR1   1k lin carbon potentiometer

Capacitors
C1   100n ceramic
C2   10n polyester
VC1   250p air spaced variable (see text)

Semiconductor
TR1   BF244 or similar N channel Jfet

Miscellaneous
T1   Toko aerial coil range 1, 2, or 3, as required
            Wire, solder, etc.

'S' Meter

A signal strength or 'S' meter is a popular feature on short wave receivers. They are useful as tuning meters and for giving comparative signal strength measurements, but they are of little value for making absolute measurements. There are agreed standards for 'S' meter calibration, but there is no realistic prospect of producing a simple DIY design that will accurately match these standards. As most users only require a meter that will provide comparative signal strength readings for the logbook, a lack of any calibration that is meaningful in absolute terms is probably of no great significance.

The full circuit diagram for the 'S' meter appears in Figure 3.4. It derives its input signal from the a.g.c. circuit of the

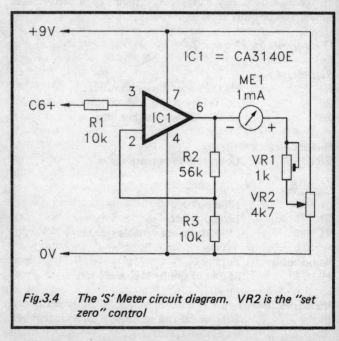

Fig.3.4   The 'S' Meter circuit diagram. VR2 is the "set zero" control

main receiver circuit, and it responds to the voltage across C6. This voltage is normally slightly positive, but strong signals take it negative. The stronger the received signal, the lower this voltage becomes. Even on a very strong signal, the actual voltage change will not be very great. The voltage swing will be no more than a few hundred millivolts.

IC1 is an operational amplifier used in the non-inverting mode, with R2 and R3 acting as the negative feedback network. These set IC1's closed loop voltage gain at between six and seven times. This gives a voltage swing at the output of IC1 of around two volts, which is sufficient to drive a moving coil panel meter. The meter (ME1) is connected in a form of bridge circuit. Under no signal conditions VR2 is adjusted so that the voltage at its wiper terminal is the same as that at the output of IC1. This gives zero voltage across the meter, and zero deflection of the pointer. When a signal is received, the output of IC1 goes to a lower voltage. The polarity of this meter is such that it gives a positive deflection from this negative voltage swing.

VR1 controls the sensitivity of the meter circuit, and it is adjusted so that very strong signals give slightly less than full scale deflection of ME1. Although R1 may seem to serve no useful purpose, it is needed to protect IC1 against input current surges. These can occur at switch-on and switch-off if the input of IC1 is fed from a capacitor (as it is in this case).

Construction of this circuit presents no difficulties, since it has only a low voltage gain and operates with d.c. signals. Bear in mind though, that IC1 is a MOSFET input component, and that it consequently requires the usual anti-static handling precautions to be observed. This mainly means fitting the device in a socket (which is something that I would recommend for all d.i.l. integrated circuits regardless of whether they are static sensitive types). Note that the CA3140E specified for IC1 is a type which will operate with a single supply rail provided negative output voltages are not needed. Most other types, including the standard μA741C and most bifet operational amplifiers, will not work in this circuit.

Although ME1 is specified as having a full scale sensitivity of 1 milliamp, meters having lower full scale sensitivities are also suitable. The choice of meters seems to be much more restricted than it was a few years ago. Presumably the popularity of digital displays has reduced the number of panel meters that are produced, leading to a more restricted choice.

High quality 'S' meters, if a suitable source can be located, usually have a full scale sensitivity of 1 milliamp, and can be used in the circuit without the need for any changes. Low cost tuning and 'S' meters, which should be perfectly adequate for use in this receiver, usually have lower full scale values — usually $200\mu A$ or $250\mu A$. These will work in the circuit, but the value of VR1 will probably need to be raised to 10k in order to permit the sensitivity of the meter circuit to be set at a suitable level.

Before switching on and testing the 'S' meter circuit, set VR1 at maximum value, and adjust VR2 so that its wiper is well towards the positive supply end of its track. At switch-on the meter should show a strong positive deflection, and VR2 must be immediately adjusted to zero the meter. VR2 has been made a panel control rather than a preset type as it is likely to need readjustment from time to time due to variations in the supply voltage. In particular, as the battery voltage drops due to ageing, VR2 will need to be readjusted to compensate for the reduced supply voltage. If the unit is powered from a stabilised mains power supply unit VR2 should only need infrequent readjustment. In fact a preset type might then be satisfactory, although I would still prefer to have VR2 as a front panel control so that any minor zeroing errors can be quickly and easily trimmed out.

The correct setting for VR1 is found by trial and error. It should be set for the lowest resistance that does not result in ME1 being driven beyond full scale deflection on very strong signals.

Components for Figure 3.4

Resistors

R1	10k 0.25 watt 5% carbon film
R2	56k 0.25 watt 5% carbon film
R3	10k 0.25 watt 5% carbon film

Potentiometers

VR1	1k sub-min preset
VR2	4k7 lin carbon potentiometer

Semiconductor
IC1   CA3140E

Miscellaneous
ME1   1mA f.s.d. 'S' meter (see text)
                   8 pin d.i.l. i.c. holder
                   Wire, solder, etc.

Audio Power Amplifier
The simple audio stage of the original receiver circuit provides
quite good results, but it only has the ability to drive a limited
range of earphones and headphones. The audio power amplifier circuit of Figure 3.5 is more versatile in that it permits
virtually any earphone or pair of headphones to be used with
the receiver. It also permits a loudspeaker to be used, and
although the output power is only a few hundred milliwatts,
it gives quite good volume. For serious DXing headphones are
definitely to be preferred, but it is useful to have the option of
loudspeaker reception when listening to local amateur stations,
DX news broadcasts on easily received European broadcast
stations, etc.

The addition of this audio power amplifier necessitates
some modifications to the original receiver circuit. The
following components should all be omitted from the original
circuit:—

                   R10, R11, R12
                   VR1
                   C9, C10, C11
                   TR4
                   SK3

R1 in this circuit connects in place of VR1 in the original
circuit. The demodulated audio signal across R1 is coupled
by C1 to volume control VR1. This couples direct to the
non-inverting input of the audio power amplifier chip, IC1.
This is an LM386N which, like many modern audio power
amplifier chips, does not require a d.c. blocking capacitor at
the input if the input connects to the earth rail. The inverting
input (pin 2) is wired to the earth rail to prevent it from

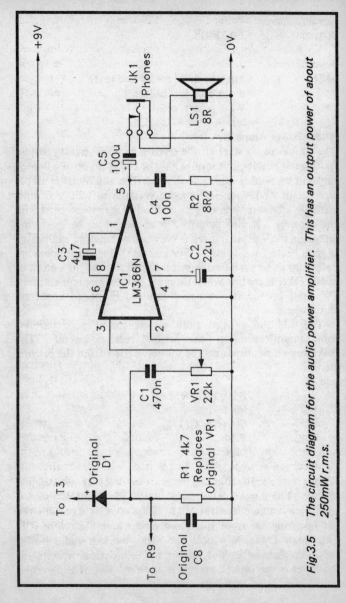

Fig.3.5   The circuit diagram for the audio power amplifier.   This has an output power of about 250mW r.m.s.

58

picking up any electrical noise. C2 decouples the supply to the preamplifier stage of IC1.

C3 acts as the d.c. blocking capacitor in a negative feedback circuit. As no resistor is used in series with C3, the circuit operates at maximum voltage gain (about 34dB). C5 provides d.c. blocking at the output while C4 and R2 are needed to aid good stability. JK1 is the headphone socket, and this has a break contact which is used to automatically disconnect the loudspeaker (LS1) when headphones are in use. The loudspeaker is a standard 8 ohm impedance type, but higher impedance units can be used. However, with higher impedance loudspeakers the maximum output power will be reduced.

Construction of the audio power amplifier presents few problems, and as the LM386N is not one of the more temperamental audio power devices, the component layout is not particularly critical. However, as with any audio power circuit, due care needs to be taken with the earth wiring. The connections to earth should be in the same order as they appear in the circuit diagram, with the supply going to LS1 first, then IC1, and finally the volume control. This should avoid any problems with earth loops and feedback through the earth wiring. The output power of the circuit is approximately 250 milliwatts r.m.s. Most miniature loudspeakers can handle this output power alright, but some very small types are only rated to take about 100 or 200 milliwatts. These are unsuitable for use with this circuit. One of about 75 millimetres in diameter should have an adequate power rating, and should give quite good volume.

The circuit should operate well when driving most types of headphones. With some low impedance types, and possibly with certain medium impedance headphones, the output might be excessive though. This makes it difficult to control the volume, and makes it all too easy to accidentally advance the volume to the point where you are practically deafened. If this problem should arise, a resistor connected in the lead from JK1 to earth should effect a cure. A value of about 100 ohms should give satisfactory results. With low or medium impedance headphones results will probably be best with the phones wired in series. Results with high impedance headphones are likely to be best with the phones wired in parallel (series connection would probably give an inadequate volume level).

Although the quiescent current consumption of the audio power amplifier is only a few milliamps, the current drain at high volume levels can be something approaching 100 milliamps. Consequently, if this circuit is included in the receiver it is essential that the set is powered from a high capacity battery such as a PP9 type. Apart from the fact that a smaller battery would have a very short operating life, it would also tend to suffer significantly from loading effects. The resultant variations in the supply voltage could noticeably affect the performance of certain circuits, particularly the local oscillator and 'S' meter circuits. This could give slightly rough sounding results during c.w. and s.s.b. reception on the high frequency bands, and slightly erratic readings from the 'S' meter. For really stable operation, a stabilised mains power supply (such as the one described later in this chapter) should be used.

Components for Figure 3.5

Resistors
R1   4k7 0.25 watt 5% carbon film
R2   8R2 0.25 watt 5% carbon film

Potentiometer
VR1   22k log carbon

Capacitors
C1   470n polyester
C2   22µ 16V elect
C3   4µ7 63V elect
C4   100n polyester
C5   100µ 10V elect

Semiconductor
IC1   LM386N

Miscellaneous
LS1   8R miniature loudspeaker (about 75mm in
              diameter)

JK1   3.5mm jack with single break contact
        8 pin d.i.l. i.c. holder
        Circuit board, wire, solder, etc.

Product Detector

Although the simple b.f.o. injection technique gives reasonable c.w. and s.s.b. reception, a simple product detector offers
a substantial improvement. The improvement in the audio
quality is not likely to be very great when using a relatively
simple product detector, but there are definite advantages in
other respects. The first of these is that the a.g.c. circuit will
work normally. The b.f.o. signal is introduced into the signal
chain after the i.f. stages. The b.f.o. and product detector
effectively replace the diode detector. However, the diode
detector can be left in circuit so that the a.g.c. action is provided in the usual way. The only pick-up of the b.f.o. signal
by the i.f. circuits is unavoidable stray coupling. It might not
be possible to totally avoid this, but it can easily be kept
down to an insignificant level.

Consequently, the b.f.o. signal will not produce a reduction
in sensitivity by activating the a.g.c. circuit. The product
detector can take quite high signal levels without becoming
overloaded, but it will be prevented from receiving really
strong signals by the a.g.c. circuit. This will prevent the
product detector from being overloaded in exactly the
same manner that it guards against overloading of the diode
detector. The a.g.c. circuit will give more consistent volume
levels on c.w. and s.s.b. signals, and will help to combat
fading. As the 'S' meter circuit operates by monitoring the
a.g.c. voltage, with a product detector in use it will indicate
the signal strengths of c.w. and s.s.b. signals properly.

The circuit diagram for the product detector appears in
Figure 3.6. This is a conventional design based on a so-called
"long-tailed pair" (TR1 and TR2). One side of the circuit is
fed with the b.f.o. signal while the other is fed with the i.f.
output signal from the secondary winding of T3. The
common emitter resistor provides a coupling between the two
transistors, and the non-linearity of the transistors provides a
crude but effective mixing and heterodyne action. The difference frequency is the required audio output signal. C3 filters

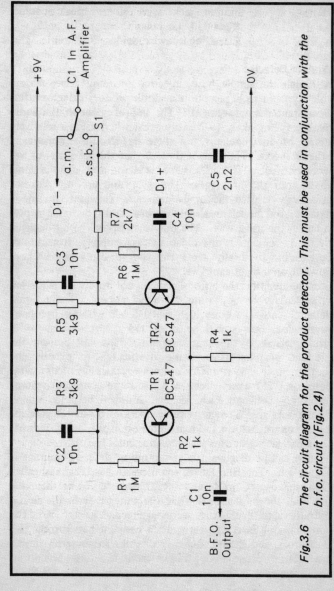

Fig.3.6   The circuit diagram for the product detector. This must be used in conjunction with the b.f.o. circuit (Fig.2.4)

62

out the sum and input signals to leave only the required audio signal. Some additional filtering was found to be necessary in order to avoid instability in the audio power amplifier, and this filtering is provided by R7 and C5. R2 was found to be necessary in order to avoid instability in the b.f.o. and product detector circuits.

S1 switches the input of the audio amplifier between the outputs of the a.m. demodulator and the product detector. This component should be a double pole type, with the other pole being used to switch off the b.f.o. when set to the a.m. mode (this pole of the switch takes the place of S1 in the b.f.o. circuit). The value of R4 has been selected to give no significant change in volume when switching from a.m. to s.s.b. or vice versa. Due to component tolerances it is just possible that there will be a small but noticeable discrepancy in the two signal levels. This can be corrected by making R4 higher in value to reduce the output level of the product detector, or lower in value to increase the output level.

Although the product detector is designed to operate in conjunction with the audio power amplifier circuit, it should work perfectly well with the simple single transistor audio stage of the original circuit. However, this stage must be modified slightly, as shown in Figure 3.7. This is basically just a matter of modifying the input section of the circuit so that the volume control no longer operates as the load resistance for the diode demodulator. This gives what is essentially the same input arrangement as that used in the audio power amplifier circuit.

The main point to keep in mind when building the product detector is that for its benefits to be gained the b.f.o. signal must not be allowed to reach the i.f. amplifier at a significant strength. The best way to avoid unwanted stray coupling is probably to have the b.f.o. and product detector reasonably well separated from the i.f. amplifier. Screening them off from one another using sheet aluminium to act as the screen can also be helpful, as can using a screened lead to carry the output signal from the b.f.o. The non-earth lead from VC3 to the main b.f.o. circuit will radiate the b.f.o. signal, and so the layout should be designed to keep this lead as short as possible.

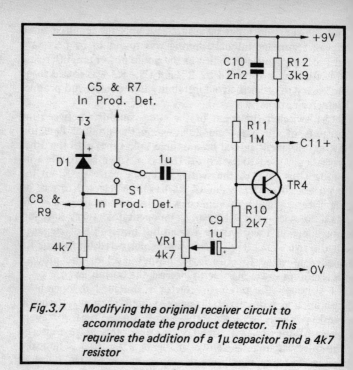

Fig.3.7   *Modifying the original receiver circuit to*
            accommodate the product detector. This
            requires the addition of a 1μ capacitor and a 4k7
            resistor

Components for Figure 3.6

Resistors

R1	1M 0.25 watt 5% carbon film
R2	1k 0.25 watt 5% carbon film
R3	3k9 0.25 watt 5% carbon film
R4	1k 0.25 watt 5% carbon film
R5	3k9 0.25 watt 5% carbon film
R6	1M 0.25 watt 5% carbon film
R7	2k7 0.25 watt 5% carbon film

Capacitors

C1	10n polyester
C2	10n polyester
C3	10n polyester

| C4 | 10n polyester |
| C5 | 2n2 polyester |

Semiconductors

| TR1 | BC547 |
| TR2 | BC547 |

Miscellaneous

S1	d.p.d.t. sub-min toggle (see text)
	Circuit board
	Wire, solder, etc.

C.W. Filter

As explained previously, obtaining the very narrow bandwidths needed for c.w. reception is not usually achieved solely by the i.f. filtering. There are actually i.f. filters which have suitably narrow bandwidths, but they are not easy to obtain, and are usually very expensive. A more popular way of handling things is to augment an ordinary a.m./s.s.b. i.f. filter with a narrow bandwidth audio filter. This method is not quite as good as using a narrow bandwidth i.f. filter, but it is much less expensive and easier.

The main drawback of an audio filter is that it appears later in the signal path than the a.g.c. circuit. This means that a strong signal very close to the wanted c.w. signal might be largely filtered out by the audio filter, but could still activate the a.g.c. circuit. This could simply reduce the volume of the c.w. signal, or if the interfering signal varies in strength, it could result in the volume of the c.w. signal varying significantly. In practice this is not usually a major problem. A reduction in the volume of the c.w. signal or variations in its volume are not likely to make it much harder to read properly. On the other hand, severely attenuating a strong interfering signal should render the signal very much easier to copy.

When using a filter of this type you should bear in mind that it has what I suppose could be termed an image response. Remember that if the filter has an operating frequency of (say) 1kHz, a signal 1kHz higher than the b.f.o. will produce a suitable audio output frequency, but so will one 1kHz below the b.f.o. frequency. In practice the b.f.o. frequency is set to one side of the i.f. filter's passband, not in the middle of it. If the b.f.o. is set on the upper side of the response, a signal 1kHz lower in frequency will be close to the centre of the passband, and will be received well. A signal 1kHz above the b.f.o. frequency will be well into one "skirt" of the filter's response, and will therefore be severely attenuated.

Just how much it is attenuated depends on the particular i.f. filter used. With the filters suggested for use in this receiver the attenuation level will be quite high, but will not totally eliminate this image response. In order to maximise attenuation of the unwanted response it is important that the b.f.o. frequency should be set well into one "skirt" of the filter's response. Using a fairly high audio filter frequency of around 2kHz also helps. With an audio filter having an operating frequency at the popular frequencies of 800Hz and 1kHz there is only 1.6kHz or 2kHz between the main response and the image one. An operating frequency of about 2kHz gives some 4kHz between the main and image responses, which is sufficient to ensure very high attenuation of the image response using any i.f. filter of reasonable quality.

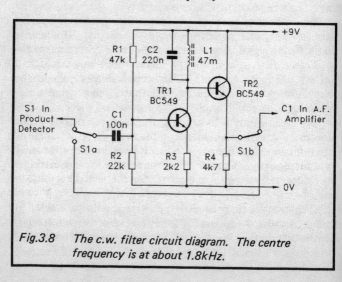

Fig.3.8   *The c.w. filter circuit diagram. The centre frequency is at about 1.8kHz.*

Figure 3.8 shows the full circuit diagram for the c.w. filter. It is assumed here that the unit will be used in conjunction with the product detector and audio power amplifier circuits. It should also work properly if it is wired between VR1 and C9 of the original receiver circuit. However, C9 in the original receiver circuit would then have to be changed to a non-polarised type (such as a polyester component).

The filter circuit is basically just a tuned amplifier based on TR1. This operates in the common emitter mode, and would normally be expected to have a very high voltage gain. However, in this case there is a large amount of local negative feedback provided by R3. This keeps the voltage gain of the circuit down to little more than unity at the centre of the passband. This enables the unit to be connected into the audio signal path without producing any mis-match problems.

C2 and L1 form a tuned circuit which acts as the collector load for TR1. This tuned circuit does not have a particularly high Q, and it is damped to some extent by the output impedance of TR1. Its performance is adequate for the present application though. Although it might seem that a narrow bandwidth filter having infinite attenuation outside the passband would be the optimum type for this application, a very sharp c.w. filter can make the receiver very difficult to use. The problem is simply one of finding c.w. signals in the first place, and relocating them if the receiver or transmission should drift. As you tune the receiver, c.w. signals seem to spring up from nowhere, and disappear as suddenly as they appeared. Any slight drift in the tuning, and signals are apt to disappear without trace.

My preference is for a slightly broader response which makes tuning far less critical, but is still very good at getting rid of unwanted signals. TR2 acts as a buffer stage at the output of the filter, and this ensures that loading effects on the tuned circuit do not result in its response becoming too broad. The specified values for L1 and C2 give a centre frequency of approximately 1.8kHz. Higher values for these two components can be used to obtain a lower centre frequency, but as already pointed out, there is an advantage in having a fairly high operating frequency.

As s.s.b. and a.m. stations are unreadable if fed through

this filter, it is obviously essential to have some means of removing it from the signal path. This can be accomplished using S1, which simply bypasses the filter when it is not required. The current consumption of the filter is about 2 milliamps, and it will obviously increase the battery drain to some extent. This can be minimised by having an additional pole of S1 connected so that it cuts off the positive supply to the filter when it is not in use. If the receiver is powered from a mains power supply circuit there is no point in doing this, and even if the receiver is battery powered you might not feel that this is worth bothering about.

The filter circuit is extremely simple and should not present any difficulties when it is being built. L1 is worthy of some explanation as this is an unusual component. The first point that has to be made is that this component must be an inductor that is suitable for operation at audio frequencies. A simple r.f. choke, if one of such a high value can be obtained, is unlikely to provide adequate performance at audio frequencies. In the prototype I used a low cost inductor based on a ferrite pot core. This is not primarily intended for operation at audio frequencies, but actually works quite well at the frequencies involved here. An alternative would be to use a component wound on a laminated iron core (as used in audio transformers). These components are intended for operation at audio frequencies, and are primarily designed for use in cross-over units in multi-way loudspeakers. Their main drawback in the current context is that they tend to be quite bulky. Also, they sometimes radiate quite strong magnetic fields which could give problems with stray feedback. An iron cored inductor should work satisfactorily, but a pot core based component, even an inexpensive type, is probably a better choice.

Components for Figure 3.8

Resistors

R1	47k 5% carbon film
R2	22k 5% carbon film
R3	2k2 5% carbon film
R4	4k7 5% carbon film.

Capacitors

C1   100n polyester
C2   220n polyester

Semiconductors

TR1   BC549
TR2   BC549

Miscellaneous

S1   d.p.d.t. min-toggle (see text)
L1   47mH a.f. choke (e.g. Cirkit type 10RB —
                          see text)
                          Circuit board, wire, solder, etc.

Mains P.S.U.

Unless portability is important, a mains power supply is a better choice than using batteries. Although the cost of the power supply unit will be higher initially, the cost of replacement batteries can soon start to mount up. A mains power supply unit gives negligible running costs, and will be cheaper in the medium and long terms. There is another advantage in using a mains power supply unit, and this is that it gives a more stable output voltage. This is reflected in better frequency stability from the local oscillator and b.f.o., and the 'S' meter circuit will need to be re-zeroed less frequently.

Figure 3.9 shows the circuit diagram for the mains power supply unit. S1 is the on/off switch, and it controls both sides of the mains supply. T1 is the mains transformer that provides safety isolation and the voltage step-down. T1 is a type which has a centre tapped secondary winding so that push-pull full wave rectification can be used. As an alternative to a 12 – 0 –12 volt transformer, a component having twin 12 volt secondary windings can be used. The secondaries are then wired in series, with the common connection acting as the 0 volt centre tap. Smoothing is provided by C1.

FS1 provides protection for T1 if there is an overload on the output or a fault in the rectifier/smoothing circuit. A fuse having a rating of 100 milliamps is suitable unless the audio power amplifier is included. The average current consumption could then easily exceed 100 milliamps with the set used at

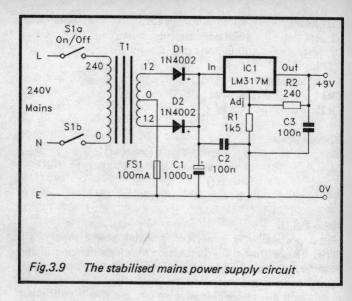

Fig.3.9   The stabilised mains power supply circuit

high volume levels, and a 250 milliamp fuse would then be a more appropriate type. FS1 should be an anti-surge type, and not the more common quick-blow variety. A quick-blow fuse could easily blow at switch-on due to the high surge current as C1 charges up.

The regulator is a three terminal type (IC1), but it is not of the usual fixed voltage variety. A fixed voltage monolithic voltage regulator would be perfectly suitable, but unfortunately, 9 volt types do not seem to be readily available. A three terminal adjustable type is therefore used, with R1 and R2 setting the output voltage at fractionally under 9 volts. If preferred, R1 can be replaced with a 2k2 preset resistor, and this can then be adjusted for an output potential of precisely 9 volts. However, provided R1 and R2 both have a tolerance of 1%, the output voltage should be quite close enough to the required figure of 9 volts. The receiver is not too fussy about the exact supply voltage, and anything from about 8 to 10 volts would be perfectly acceptable. Using 1% components for R1 and R2, the output voltage should be within 0.25 volts of the designed output potential of 9 volts.

70

The LM317 series of voltage regulators have a very high level of performance incidentally, giving the circuit a very stable and low ripple output. C2 and C3 are needed to aid good stability in IC1.

The LM317M has overload current protection, and this will protect the components in the circuit against short term overloads. As the LM317M is a 500 milliamp component, but T1 is only rated at 250 milliamps, long term overloads on the output could result in T1 burning out. Overloads of this type should obviously be avoided. The LM317T (1 amp version) is also suitable for operation in this circuit, and is probably easier to obtain than the LM317M. However, as its current limiting comes into operation at a higher current, severe overloads on the output could rapidly lead to T1 overheating. The LM317M is to be preferred in this particular application. The LM317L (100 milliamp version) would appear to be suitable if the receiver is not equipped with the audio power amplifier stage. In practice an LM317L might tend to operate quite hot, and the LM317M is a safer choice.

Construction of this circuit is not particularly difficult, but as the mains supply is involved it is essential to take due care when designing the component layout and building the unit. All the usual safety precautions should be scrupulously observed. In particular, as the receiver will presumably have a metal case and chassis, these must be earthed to the mains earth lead. The case must have a screw fitting lid or cover rather than clip-on type, so that there is no easy way of gaining access to the dangerous mains wiring. Ideally, the connections to the on/off switch and any other exposed mains wiring should be insulated with p.v.c. sleeving.

For C2 and C3 to be effective, they should be mounted as close as possible to IC1, as should R1 and R2. R2 has an unusual value at 240 ohms, but this is in the E24 series of values, and should be available from most component retailers. The mains transformer and the mains wiring tend to radiate quite strong mains "hum", and they should be kept as well separated from the rest of the unit as is reasonably possible. In particular, try to keep the power supply and audio circuits well separated.

Before connecting the output of the power supply unit to

the receiver it would be prudent to use a multimeter to check the supply's output voltage. This should be within a few hundred millivolts of the nominal 9 volt output potential. If there is a significant error, switch off at once, disconnect the unit from the mains supply, and recheck all the wiring very thoroughly.

Components for Figure 3.9

Resistors

R1	1k5 0.25 watt 1% metal film
R2	240R 0.25 watt 1% metal film

Capacitors

C1	1000µ 25V elect
C2	100n ceramic
C3	100n ceramic

Semiconductors

IC1	LM317M
D1	1N4002
D2	1N4002

Miscellaneous

S1	Rotary mains switch
FS1	100mA 20mm anti-surge (see text)
T1	mains primary, 12 − 0 − 12 volt 250mA secondary (or twin 12-volt 250mA secondaries wired in series)
	Circuit board
	20mm panel mounting fuse holder
	Control knob, wire, solder, etc.

Finally

If the basic short wave superhet is augmented with all the add-ons featured in this chapter, the result is a receiver having the stages shown in the block diagram of Figure 3.10. In short wave receiver terms this set will be very inexpensive, but it should provide excellent results for a.m. reception on the broadcast bands, or c.w./s.s.b. reception on the amateur bands.

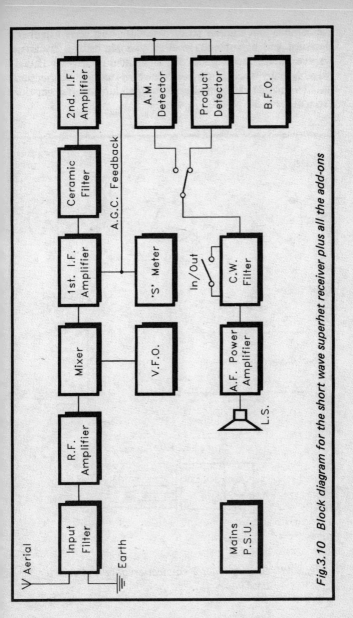

Fig.3.10 Block diagram for the short wave superhet receiver plus all the add-ons

Remember that the key to success with short wave listening is patience and persistence, whether you are using a crystal set or the latest ready-made digital wonder receiver. If used sensibly, any version of the receiver described in this book should provide many hours of fun listening to transmissions from all over the world.

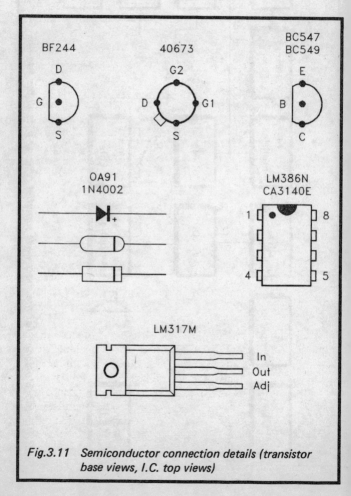

Fig.3.11 *Semiconductor connection details (transistor base views, I.C. top views)*